Welcome

The history of space is a heroic one – it takes courage to climb aboard a rocket and head out beyond the atmosphere, especially if you're one of the first pioneers to do so. But space exploration has other heroes apart from the brave astronauts and cosmonauts who were the first to leave the Earth. They wouldn't have been able to do so without the pioneering work of generations of scientists who tackled the complex theories of astrophysics and the logistics of space travel, sometimes persisting in the face of condemnation and censure. In *Heroes of Space*, you'll meet some of the people who have made space exploration possible. Some of them are easy to define as heroes: they took on exceptional challenges and some of them made the ultimate sacrifice. Others have more complex legacies borne out of World War II, the Cold War, and the Space Race. All of them, however, made an outstanding contribution to the scientific programmes that made humankind's ancient dream a 20th century reality, putting humans into orbit and on the Moon, changing humanity's view of ourselves forever, and setting us on the road to one day exploring the rest of our Solar System and maybe even beyond.

FUTURE

HEROES OF SPACE

Future PLC Quay House, The Ambury, Bath, BA1 1UA

Heroes of Space Editorial
Editor **April Madden**
Senior Designer **Adam Markiewicz**
Senior Art Editor **Andy Downes**
Head of Art & Design **Greg Whitaker**
Editorial Director **Jon White**

All About Space Editorial
Editor in Chief **Gemma Lavender**
Art Editor **Jon Wells**

Cover images
NASA, Alamy

Photography
All copyrights and trademarks are recognised and respected

Advertising
Media packs are available on request
Commercial Director **Clare Dove**

International
Head of Print Licensing **Rachel Shaw**
licensing@futurenet.com
www.futurecontenthub.com

Circulation
Head of Newstrade **Tim Mathers**

Production
Head of Production **Mark Constance**
Production Project Manager **Matthew Eglinton**
Advertising Production Manager **Joanne Crosby**
Digital Editions Controller **Jason Hudson**
Production Managers **Keely Miller, Nola Cokely,
Vivienne Calvert, Fran Twentyman**

Printed by William Gibbons, 26 Planetary Road,
Willenhall, West Midlands, WV13 3XT

Distributed by Marketforce, 5 Churchill Place, Canary Wharf, London, E14 5HU
www.marketforce.co.uk Tel: 0203 787 9001

All About Space Heroes of Space First Edition (ASB3919)
© 2021 Future Publishing Limited

**Connectors.
Creators.
Experience
Makers.**

Future plc is a public
company quoted on the
London Stock Exchange
(symbol: FUTR)
www.futureplc.com

Chief executive **Zillah Byng-Thorne**
Non-executive chairman **Richard Huntingford**
Chief financial officer **Rachel Addison**

Tel +44 (0)1225 442 244

Part of the

All About Space
bookazine series

**Widely
Recycled**

For press freedom
with responsibility

Contents

22

46

102

8 **Secret lives of space's greatest heroes**
Six men and women who made groundbreaking contributions

15 **The rocket man: Wernher von Braun**
From German bomb maker to putting man on the Moon

18 **Sending Sputnik to space**
The first winner of the Space Race began an era of exploration

22 **Lives of the animal astronauts**
The creatures who paved the way for humans in space

30 **The beginning of NASA: Project Mercury**
NASA's first major project and the astronauts who worked on it

34 **Alan Shepard - the first American in space**
The first American in space made history for the USA and paved the way for Space Race success

38 **Interview: Wallace "Wally" Funk**
In 1961, air ace Wally hoped to become a female astronaut

42 **The first man in space**
Yuri Gagarin's stellar start to the Space Race

46 **Was he really first?**
Were there cosmonauts who went up before Yuri Gagarin?

54 **Project Gemini: Learning to fly**
The bridge between early efforts and the Moon landings

58 **Valentina Tereshkova**
How a girl from a textile factory reached the stars

64 **Gemini 8: Mission abort**
From successfully docking two crafts to a horrifying problem...

66 **Margaret Hamilton: the software genius**
The Apollo coder reveals the secrets behind the programme

70 **Fire in the cockpit**
The tragic loss of the first Apollo craft - and nearly the programme

72 **The secrets of Apollo 11**
Buzz Aldrin and others reveal the unpublished archives

80 **Houston, we've had a problem**
Apollo 13 gripped the world's attention for all the wrong reasons

82 **Carl Sagan**
The influential visions of scientist Carl Sagan

88 **What we learned from the Challenger disaster**
A terrible tragedy that ultimately changed NASA for the better

94 **What we learned from the Columbia disaster**
How this awful incident forced a reckoning on safety measures

102 **Stephen Hawking**
Remembering the world's greatest scientist and his incredible work

118 **NASA's most dangerous missions**
Astronauts recount their scariest moments in space

APOLLO 11
MISSION
TO THE MOON
p72

SECRET LIVES OF SPACE'S GREATEST HEROES

These six men and women made groundbreaking contributions to our understanding of the universe, and their stories are often linked in surprising ways

Written by Giles Sparrow

Galileo Galilei

The great Italian astronomer and physicist Galileo inherited his interest in science from his musical father. Vincenzo Galilei specialised in the lute, a distant relative of modern guitars, and was also a musical theorist who used experimentation and mathematics to identify a new law that correctly described the relationship between the tension on a string and its musical pitch. Vincenzo's discoveries helped to inspire his son's mathematical approach to problems of 'natural philosophy' and foreshadowed Galileo's own struggles to overturn outdated views of the world.

At age 17, Galileo became a student in the University at Pisa, training in medicine at his father's suggestion. He made his first great discovery – that a pendulum has a regular period regardless of the width of its oscillations – while watching a swinging lamp in Pisa Cathedral, and had soon turned it into a practical device for measuring a patient's pulse. After persuading his father to let him pursue his interest in mathematics, he became a professor by the age of 25.

Throughout his life, Galileo was perpetually short of cash. His father's death left him responsible for his mother and three younger siblings – and later his own partner and three children. He boosted his income by taking in private students and selling his inventions, and later took a better paid job at Padua in the Republic of Venice. It was here in 1609 that he got word of an amazing new invention from the Netherlands – the telescope.

Galileo immediately set out to make a telescope of his own, using lenses mounted at either end of a card tube. Thanks to his talents for maths and experimentation, he soon found ways of improving on the basic idea. When he showed it to the Venetian rulers, they offered to double his salary

and pay handsomely for the instrument itself. Within a few months, the course of Galileo's life was fatefully changed as he turned his telescope to the sky and made a series of discoveries including mountains on the Moon, countless faint stars and four small moons circling Jupiter. These findings undermined the traditional view that everything in the universe circled Earth – Nicolaus Copernicus, a Polish priest, had suggested the idea of a Sun-centred universe in 1543, but until now there had been no observational evidence to back it up.

Galileo's account of his discoveries in his book *The Starry Messenger* turned him into a scientific celebrity, but from 1613 onwards his arguments in support of the Copernican model put him on a collision course with the Roman Catholic Church. Powerful connections helped to protect him at first, but an argumentative nature got him into repeated trouble, and his 1632 *Dialogue Concerning the Two Chief World Systems* led to a trial before the inquisition and a sentence of house arrest for the rest of his life. Nevertheless, he continued to make important contributions to the foundations of modern physics right up until his death in 1642.

Above: Galileo clashed with the Catholic Church by siding with Copernicus' heliocentric Solar System

Galileo's planet: Jupiter

Jupiter is the Solar System's largest planet. Its volume is 1,321-times larger than Earth's and its mass is 318 times ours.

It's named after the Roman god Jupiter, the god of sky and thunder.

It's the fourth-brightest object in the sky after the Sun, Moon and Venus.

Jupiter has 53 confirmed moons, its four largest being Io, Europa, Callisto and Ganymede.

The 'King of the Solar System' has faint dusty rings. They weren't discovered until 1979.

The Great Red Spot on Jupiter is a storm that's large enough to engulf the Earth. It's been swirling for at least 300 years.

It has the fastest rotation in the Solar System, completing a spin in less than ten hours – fast enough to cause a bulge at the equator.

It's difficult to pinpoint when Jupiter was discovered – being visible to the naked eye, records date back to the 7th or 8th century CE.

William Herschel

No one knows quite when William became interested in astronomy, but his sister Caroline's memoirs recall him discussing the night sky with her on their journey to England. Shortly after their arrival, he began building his own telescopes - at first simply by assembling lenses obtained by local glassmakers, but later, as his needs grew more demanding, by casting mirrors and building reflecting telescopes of his own design.

Eventually, William had instruments that were fit for his plans - not just to observe the night sky, but to carry out detailed surveys in search of comets and other undiscovered objects. His telescopes were the best of their age, and his reputation soon began to spread. His first project involved a systematic catalogue of closely spaced stars, with William spending all his available nights at the eyepiece and Caroline making careful notes. At the time most people assumed that stars were randomly scattered through space, but the discovery of numerous close pairs convinced him otherwise. There were too many to be accounted for by chance alignments, so some of them at least must be paired binary stars in orbit around each other.

In March 1781, William spotted the planet now called Uranus. When he first saw the spherical bluish blob in the constellation of Taurus, he assumed it was a comet - it was Astronomer Royal Nevil Maskelyne who began to wonder whether the unusually solid-looking object might be a planet beyond Saturn. A few months later, continued tracking of the object's movement confirmed that it was indeed a remote planet. Herschel suggested naming it George's Star - after King George III - and the king returned the honour by naming William his personal astronomer and granting him a salary of £200 on condition that he moved to Windsor, with an additional £50 for Caroline to work as his assistant. The Herschels, both brother and sister, abandoned their musical careers to become some of Europe's first professional scientists. They would go on to make countless other discoveries.

Right: Herschel was trained as a musician and joined the army at just 14 years of age

Upper atmosphere haze
The highest parts of Uranus' atmosphere are thought to contain haze made up of hydrocarbons that obscures features lower in the atmosphere.

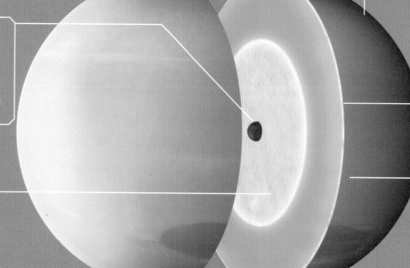

Inside Uranus

Planetary core
Uranus' core extends to about a fifth of the planet's full diameter, and is made of rock, ice and silica. Its temperature is thought to be around 5,000°C (9,032°F).

Icy mantle
This isn't ice as we know it. Uranus' mantle is made up of a hot, dense fluid scientists refer to as a water-ammonia ocean.

Potential heat-trapping layer
Scientists have not confirmed the existence of a layer around Uranus' ice layer trapping heat and making it appear cooler, but one could have formed during a giant impact.

Atmosphere
Uranus looks bluish-green through a telescope thanks to the methane in its atmosphere. It also contains hydrogen, helium, acetylene and other hydrocarbons.

Henrietta Swan Leavitt

Several remarkable female astronomers played a key role in establishing our understanding of the stars in the late-19th and early 20th centuries, and Henrietta Swan Leavitt was arguably the most important of them all, laying the foundations for a revolution in our view of the entire universe.

Leavitt was born in 1868 to a well-off Massachusetts family. After displaying an early academic talent, she studied at Oberlin College in Ohio and Harvard University's Society for the Collegiate Instruction of Women (later Radcliffe College). Although she showed a talent for mathematics, she did not take a course in astronomy until her fourth year of university.

After graduating in 1892 – without a degree since at the time they were not awarded to women – Henrietta pursued her newfound interest in the heavens by applying to work at Harvard College Observatory. Here, astronomer Edward Charles Pickering was assembling a team of women to catalogue and analyse data being gathered by the first photographic survey of the sky. Work was often published under Pickering's name with little acknowledgement of the women behind the scenes. Nevertheless, the so-called 'Harvard Computers' would make huge contributions to our understanding of the structure and evolution of stars.

Henrietta's particular speciality was the analysis of variable stars – measuring how their brightness fluctuated between photographic plates taken on different nights and trying to identify patterns. However, her career was somewhat intermittent, with frequent breaks for travel, family responsibilities and for the good of her delicate health and overstrained eyesight.

It was in 1904 that she turned her attention to new plates sent from the observatory's Southern Hemisphere outpost at Arequipa in Peru. These images showed the Small Magellanic Cloud (SMC) – a crowded clump of stars near the southern Milky Way. Here, Leavitt found and analysed more than 1,770 new variable stars. Among them, she spotted 16 with a distinctive cycle of changing light that suggested they were related.

In a 1908 paper reporting her discoveries, she noted that among these stars, the brighter ones had longer periods. Because stars in the cloud could be assumed to lie at the same distance from Earth, their apparent brightness in photographs would be a reflection of their true physical brightness, or 'luminosity', something that wasn't true for stars randomly scattered elsewhere in the sky.

After identifying several more stars to conclusively prove the link, Henrietta published her 'period-luminosity relationship' in a paper of 1912. The implications were huge: astronomers soon realised that Henrietta's stars were of a familiar type known as Cepheids, and this meant that the relative distances of similar stars elsewhere in the sky could be worked out.

Henrietta succumbed to stomach cancer in 1921, before the full implications of her work became clear. Just four years later, Edwin Hubble found and measured Cepheid variables embedded in some of the mysterious 'spiral nebulae' that dotted the sky. He showed that they were fainter even than those in the SMC, and conclusively proved that the nebulae are actually galaxies far beyond the Milky Way. Today, Cepheids remain a vital rung on the cosmic-distance ladder used to measure the scale of the universe.

> "Henrietta's particular speciality was the analysis of variable stars"

Einstein's greatest letters

A letter sent to U.S. President Franklin D. Roosevelt, signed by Albert Einstein, details uranium as a new and important source of energy in the "immediate future"

Albert Einstein pens a romantic letter to Russian spy Margarita Konenkova

This signed letter dates back to 1928 and concerns the formalisation of the 'Third Stage of the Theory of Relativity'

A letter signed by Albert Einstein to Ernst Gabor Strauss about the unified field theory

© Lucien Aigner / Getty

Albert Einstein

Above: Einstein is best known for his work surrounding the speed of light and relativity

Right: Eddington made crucial observations of stars around the Sun during a total eclipse

Born in Ulm, southern Germany, in 1879, Albert Einstein would become the most famous physicist of the 20th century, introducing revolutionary ideas that transformed all of science - and astronomy in particular.

Einstein showed his remarkable talents from an early age, reading widely and mastering tricky mathematical fields such as algebra and Euclidean geometry before he was a teenager. However, the young Albert grew restless with the dull curriculum and regimented teaching methods, and eventually ditched school entirely, completing his education in Switzerland some time later.

After graduating from the Federal Polytechnic School in Zürich, Einstein was frustrated in his search for a teaching post of his own. Eventually, after taking Swiss citizenship - also a way of avoiding German military service - he found employment at the Bern patent office, in a job that left him with plenty of spare time to work on his PhD and consider the questions that he was really interested in.

In 1905, Einstein stepped into the limelight with the publication of not one, but four groundbreaking scientific papers. One provided long-sought-after direct proof of the existence of atoms. Another laid the foundations for what would become known as quantum physics, but it was the other two that transformed our view of the universe itself.

Einstein's breakthrough came from confronting questions about the speed of light, which always seemed to be the same regardless of the relative motions of the light source and the measuring device. Physicists had put forward many possible explanations for this troubling phenomenon, but all relied on it being a kind of illusion, and none of them were satisfactory.

Einstein, however, dared to ask if the speed of light really is constant, regardless of relative motion. He showed that the consequences for everyday life would be unnoticeable, but that in 'relativistic' situations, with an observer and an object or light source moving at near-light speed relative to each other, strange effects would occur. From the observer's point of view, objects at near light speed appear to become shorter and to experience time more slowly.

Further consideration led Einstein to conclude that accelerating objects already at relativistic

> "Einstein showed his remarkable talents from an early age, mastering tricky mathematical fields"

speeds will tend to increase their mass rather than their speed – since the speed of light itself is unreachable – and this led in turn to the famous equation $E=mc^2$.

Einstein's ideas were hugely influential, but Albert himself was already pondering the next big question. So far he had only formulated a 'special theory of relativity' where the observer and object moved at high relative speed, but did not accelerate or decelerate. He now realised that acceleration was effectively the same as being in a gravitational field, so a description of 'general relativity' would also automatically be a description of gravity itself.

Einstein's theory of general relativity, when it emerged, showed that the presence of large masses can have effects similar to those seen in special relativity, distorting our measurements of time and space. However, its publication in 1916, as Europe tore itself apart in the First World War, meant it was widely overlooked.

It was only in 1919, following the return of peace, that astronomer Sir Arthur Eddington was able to journey to Africa and make crucial observations of stars around the Sun during a solar eclipse. These revealed the effect we now call gravitational lensing in the form of a slight distortion in the measured positions of the stars as light is deflected due to the Sun's distortion of nearby space and time. Einstein was proved right, opening the way for a new era in physics, and eventually for powerful new astronomical techniques that make use of his discoveries and predictions.

Cecilia Payne-Gaposchkin

It was while studying at Newnham College, Cambridge, in 1919 that Cecilia Payne-Gaposchkin's interest in astronomy was ignited by a lecture from Sir Arthur Eddington on Einstein's new science of general relativity. Determined to follow her newfound passion after leaving Cambridge, she applied to Harvard College Observatory. Alongside images of the sky, the Observatory's catalogue also included the spectra of countless stars, made by spreading out starlight according to its wavelength and capturing it on photographic plates. These rainbow-like bands were usually crossed by a variety of dark 'absorption lines' – chemical fingerprints created by the light-absorbing properties of various elements somehow associated with the stars themselves. The goal of her PhD thesis would be to explain exactly how.

One of the most puzzling aspects of stellar spectra was the huge variety in the strength and number of their absorption lines, implying great variation in the elements they contained – by proper application of the equation, Cecilia was able to show that most of this variety was due to differences in the surface temperature of the stars, not to their composition. Higher temperatures strip away more of the electrons from around atoms in a star's atmosphere, leaving 'ions' with increasingly positive electric charges that interact differently with light escaping from the star's surface.

Applying these principles to the atmospheres of various stars, Payne showed that they contained similar amounts of relatively heavy elements such as silicon, carbon and oxygen to those found on Earth. But there was a troubling discrepancy when it came to the lightest elements: helium and especially hydrogen seemed to be vastly more abundant in the stars than they are on Earth.

Throughout a long and distinguished career spent entirely at Harvard, Cecilia was able to see the fruits of her breakthrough in understanding the composition of stars. Understanding that they are predominantly made of hydrogen is the key to understanding the fuel source that powers them, the conditions inside them and the various tracks along which they can evolve during their lifetimes.

Above: Payne anaylsed the spectra of stars and unlocked the secrets of stellar composition

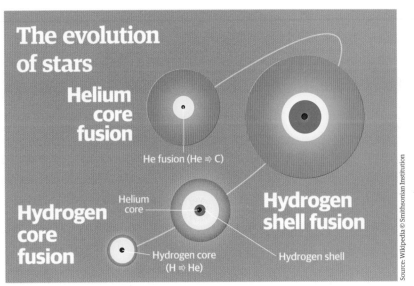

Katherine Johnson

Katherine grew up in the southern United States at a time when racial segregation was commonplace and opportunities for African Americans, male or female, were in short supply. In 1952, Katherine learned that the National Advisory Committee for Aeronautics (NACA) was looking to hire mathematicians. At first she was assigned to the group of black women 'computers' who did the number-crunching to analyse data gathered from NACA's research aircraft. Her particular talent was soon recognised, however, with a temporary posting within an all-male, all-white team at the Flight Research Division that became permanent.

After the surprise launch of the Soviet Union's Sputnik satellite in 1957, chaotic US attempts to play 'catch up' culminated in a wholesale reorganisation of NACA to form the nucleus of the current NASA. Racial and gender segregation were done away with, while the Flight Research Division was renamed the Space Task Group and was charged with putting American astronauts into orbit ahead of the Soviets. Katharine was therefore in the right place at the right time to play a key role in the early US space effort. As well as working on Alan Shepard's Freedom 7 suborbital flight in 1961, she co-authored work on the precise placement of satellites in particular orbits and the relationship between a spacecraft's re-entry point and its landing site.

Despite machine-based calculation fast becoming the norm at NASA, the early 'Mercury 7' astronauts were reluctant to put their lives entirely in the hands of technology, and John Glenn famously asked for Katherine to manually recheck the calculations before the launch of his Friendship 7 spacecraft on the first US orbital mission.

Johnson continued to work at NASA until her retirement in 1986. She considered her proudest achievement to be the calculations needed to sync the Apollo Lunar Module with the orbiting Command Module. She also helped devise a method of 'navigation by the stars' that allowed the astronauts of the crippled Apollo 13 spacecraft to time the precise engine burn needed to return them safely to Earth. In 2015, she was awarded the Presidential Medal of Freedom by US President Barack Obama, while the next year, her story, along with those of other black American women at Langley, was chronicled in Margot Lee Shetterly's book *Hidden Figures*.

Johnson's Apollo 11 code

74
Memory (ROM) of the Apollo guidance computer, in kilobytes

1202
The first of several 1202 and 1201 computer alarms began to sound when Armstrong ignited the descent engine on the lunar lander

9
Early versions of the Sony Walkman portable cassette recorders were flown on the Apollo missions

6.7
The diameter of the Saturn V computer in metres

36
Weight of satellites launched by Apollo in kilograms

©NASA

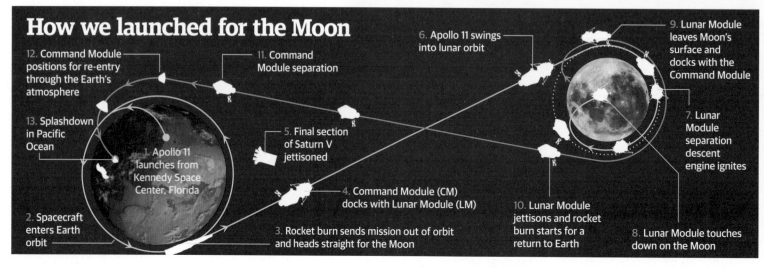

How we launched for the Moon

12. Command Module positions for re-entry through the Earth's atmosphere

13. Splashdown in Pacific Ocean

1. Apollo 11 launches from Kennedy Space Center, Florida

2. Spacecraft enters Earth orbit

11. Command Module separation

5. Final section of Saturn V jettisoned

4. Command Module (CM) docks with Lunar Module (LM)

3. Rocket burn sends mission out of orbit and heads straight for the Moon

6. Apollo 11 swings into lunar orbit

9. Lunar Module leaves Moon's surface and docks with the Command Module

7. Lunar Module separation descent engine ignites

10. Lunar Module jettisons and rocket burn starts for a return to Earth

8. Lunar Module touches down on the Moon

Katherine Johnson's mathematical prowess was directly instrumental in the Apollo programme and the Moon landings, and was foundational in NASA's ongoing missions

The rocket man

Wernher von Braun started his career as a Nazi scientist, but ended it after putting the USA on the Moon

Written by April Madden

Apollo 11 lifting off on the Saturn V rocket that was von Braun's brainchild and lifelong dream

Wernher von Braun was a leading light in NASA's rocketry programme. His work put man on the Moon

The German civilian on the bicycle approached tentatively. It was 2 May 1945 in a small Austrian village. Far away in Berlin, Nazi Germany was falling to the Allied forces. That was where the action was. There was little chance of glory for a private of the US 44th Infantry in this backwater. Then the German spoke, hesitantly, in halting English. "Hello? My name is Magnus von Braun. My brother invented the V-2. We want to surrender."

US High Command were delighted. The man's brother was Wernher von Braun, leading light in the Nazi weapons development programme. The V-2 rocket he had invented was extraordinary; an unmanned, guided ballistic missile, capable of delivering death from 200 miles away. There were even whispers that his technology could broach the edge of space itself. They may have been mere rumours, but the Americans were confident that their new guest was soon going to tell them everything that they wanted to know. And he did.

Wernher von Braun was born on 23 March 1912 in Wirsitz, a small town in what is now Poland. His family were upper class and well-to-do; his father was a government minister during the Weimar Republic, and the family lived in Berlin. Wernher was a clever boy – he played piano and cello and had early ambitions to be a composer. But when his mother bought him a telescope, he realised his destiny lay with the stars. In 1924 at the age of 12, he was arrested after blowing up a toy car in a busy Berlin street. He'd attached fireworks to it, in a schoolboy attempt at making a rocket. Despite his precocity, however, Wernher was failing mathematics and physics, until he read Hermann Oberth's book *By Rocket into Planetary Space*, which taught him their importance. Years later, he explained: "Hermann Oberth was the first, who when thinking about the possibility of spaceships, grabbed a slide-rule and presented mathematically analysed concepts and designs... I, myself, owe to him not only the guiding-star of my life, but also my first contact with the theoretical and practical aspects of rocketry

A US Army diagram of a V-2 rocket showing the game changing engineering created by von Braun and his team

16

Wernher von Braun poses with the engines of a Saturn V rocket. The Saturn V powered the Apollo programme

Taken during the launch of Apollo 11, this photo shows von Braun during the launch of the mission that would see his dream of sending a manned rocket to the Moon come true

Nazi controversy

Just how far did von Braun's Nazi connection extend?

Wernher von Braun maintained throughout his life that he was not a Nazi, although like many members of the German intellectual elite, he was a member of the Party. He explained in an affidavit to US forces that: "In 1939, I was officially demanded to join the National Socialist Party. At this time I was already Technical Director at the Army Rocket Centre at Peenemünde (Baltic Sea). The technical work carried out there had, in the meantime, attracted more and more attention in higher levels. Thus, my refusal to join the party would have meant that I would have to abandon the work of my life. Therefore, I decided to join. My membership in the Party did not involve any political activity." However, German records show that he in fact joined the party in 1937. Whether von Braun was mistaken or lying in his affidavit is still a matter of debate.

The German V-2 rockets were built using slave labour from the concentration camps of World War II and von Braun was certainly aware of this. He described conditions in the plant where the rockets were built as "repulsive" but claimed never to have seen prisoners beaten. Several concentration camp survivors came forward in later years to counter this claim, but the allegations were never proven. Wernher von Braun did not, however, deny that he was aware of the brutality of the camps and the slave labour regime that built the German rockets, but did state that he felt powerless to do anything about the terrible conditions.

d space travel". Enthusiasm renewed, he began ursuing the subjects in earnest, and excelled at em. He studied physics, chemistry and astronomy, d was working on his doctorate in physics when e Nazi Party came to power.

Weapons research and development was forbidden Germany under the terms of the Treaty of ersailles that had ended World War I, but for some ason, rocketry had been overlooked, so von Braun uld legitimately study it. His doctoral research as immediately classified by the armed forces, and tensibly von Braun was given little choice about s absorption into their ranks. He later claimed that e was effectively ordered to join both the SS and e Nazi Party, and he was certainly given no choice er being moved to a development facility in the dustrial area of Peenemünde, where he began to udy and develop rocket technology in earnest. hen a colour movie of his V-2 rocket was presented Adolf Hitler, the enthusiastic Führer personally ade von Braun a professor. Despite this success, he as aware that the paranoid Nazi command could ange its mind at any time. He was arrested in 44 – an informer had claimed that he'd complained a dinner party that he wasn't able to work on spaceship – and held for two weeks, until his pervisors secured his release.

Aware that the war effort was now going badly r Germany, von Braun spoke to other staff at the enemünde facility and gave them a stark choice: rrender to the Americans or to the Soviets. The erman rocket team, aware that their SS guards had ders to kill them if any enemy approached, decided take a chance on the USA. When they were spersed into the Austrian hills during the last days the war, they took their chance to run straight to the Americans' arms. The team surrendered en asse; Wernher von Braun was placed under the re of US and British troops at Kransberg Castle in esse, where German scientists were being debriefed. espite his surrender to the US, it's alleged that von raun was initially debriefed by a British team that cluded Britain's leading rocket engineer LS Snell, ventor of the Concorde supersonic jet engine. What actly von Braun discussed with the British has ever been revealed.

Evacuated to the US as part of Operation Paperclip, which the US offered new lives to Nazi scientists exchange for their continued research, von Braun d his team eventually ended up in Fort Bliss, exas. Jokingly referring to themselves as "prisoners

This photograph was taken shortly after von Braun surrendered to American forces in 1945

of peace", they continued their work, despite a lack of finance for both their research and their living quarters. The Korean War saw a change in their fortunes: they were transferred to Alabama, where they began work on the famous Redstone rocket. Frustratingly though, throughout the 1950s, the Soviet Union, inspired by von Braun's V-2 rockets, were always one step ahead of him. When the Soviets won the first stage of the Space Race by putting the Sputnik satellite in orbit, the US created its state-funded space agency, NASA. Wernher von Braun was transferred to the nascent agency in 1960, with the aim of putting the Americans back in pole position. Despite finally being able to work on his dream project – a rocket bound for space – von Braun was apparently overly cautious. His focus on fixing technical issues before the test flights that would allow his rocket design to be certified safe for human flight delayed NASA's efforts, resulting in the Soviets being the first to put a man in space.

Wernher von Braun did eventually achieve his goal – his Saturn V rockets put the Apollo missions on the Moon – but despite reaching the rank of Deputy Associate Administrator for Planning at NASA, he always felt that his vision for conquering the stars was at odds with the American government's waning interest in the space programme once the Moon had been reached. He retired from NASA in 1972 and died in 1977.

Wernher von Braun with Fritz Todt, a German engineer notorious for his use of forced labour programmes

Wernher von Braun (in non-military attire) with Nazi officers in 1941

Sending Sputnik to space

Designed in a race against the Americans, the Soviet Union not only crossed the finish line, but with the launch of a simple satellite, began an era of space exploration

Written by Scott Dutfield

It was the satellite that fired the starting gun for the Space Race between two world powers. Designed to simply observe the Earth's atmosphere, Sputnik began a wave of technological achievements and became the Soviet Union's national treasure.

Following the end of the Second World War, both the United States and the Soviet Union had entered into the Cold War, beginning in 1947. A political and economic battle placed the nations at loggerheads. Both focused on the development of advanced military weaponry, including the creation of intercontinental ballistic missile (ICBM) technologies. Taking inspiration from the Germans' explosive endeavour, the V-2 rocket, the possibilities for nuclear warhead missiles became a growing concern and goal for both nations. However, in the early 1950s, sights were set on the heavens due to the role rockery could play in entering a new field of exploration - space.

After a period of global diversity during the war, in 1952 National Academy of Science member Lloyd Berker proposed to the International Council of Scientific Unions (ICSU) a series of global geophysical activities. The project aimed to conduct a series of collaborative studies to further understand the Earth and its environment over a fixed period of time. Running from July 1957 to December 1958, this window of scientific exploration was known as the International Geophysical Year (IGY). From glaciation to gravity, over 70 countries took part in projects that would lead to the understanding of plate tectonics and polar regions and the discovery of the Van Allen radiation belt.

In July 1955, United States President Dwight Eisenhower announced the country's aim to launch an artificial satellite as part of the IGY, stating that: "The most important result of the International Geophysical Year is the demonstration of the ability of peoples of all nations to work together harmoniously for the common good. I hope this can become a common practice in other fields of human endeavour." Seeing this announcement as a challenge, the Soviet Union followed suit, announcing its plans to achieve the same feat a month later. The rebuttal, however, was not based on an existing project already in motion, rather a consequence of the Cold War.

The Second World War had played host to the latest rockery weapons. However, none of these were capable of launching a satellite. In order to achieve this astronomical feat of engineering, a satellite would first need a way to surpass the

History was made in 1957 as mankind's first artificial satellite, Sputnik, reached space

The former USSR released a commemorative stamp to celebrate Sputnik's success

A case of mistaken identity

Flying high in the sky, many thought their gaze had caught a glimpse of a passing satellite. However, not all was as it seemed

Met with the announcement of the first satellite launched into space, many people in both the Soviet Union and the United States rushed outside to see Sputnik for themselves. Due to Sputnik's aluminium appearance, the elliptical satellite often found itself catching the Sun's rays, illuminating its position in the sky. In fact, Sputnik was so reflective it could be seen from Earth's surface through a pair of binoculars – and if bright enough even the naked eye. Accompanied with its onboard radio beacon, Sputnik's shiny surface could also be used to locate its position around the globe during orbit.

Curiosity and concern over the satellite's existence formed a following of public observers, each trying to catch a glimpse of the revolutionary tech. On one fateful day in late 1957 officials received a rush of sightings claiming to see Sputnik clearly in the sky. However, their mass excitement is believed to have been the result of misidentification. In fact, what was thought to be Sputnik was indeed the rocket that had sent the satellite to space, the R-7. Sputnik wasn't alone in reaching orbit, because the rocket's 26-metre-long core stage went with it. It was also covered in reflective panels, placed for visual tracking of the rockets return. The rocket fell back to Earth in December 1957, aligning with the reported sighting.

Researchers used Sputnik's beeps and calculated trajectory to track its movements around the Earth

Sputnik's rise to fame resulted in the creation of toys to show the next generation Sputnik's triumphal orbit of the Earth

Earth's gravitational pull. Recognised as a leading expert in aeronautical engineering, Sergei Korolev, chief designer in the field, was a natural fit for undertaking the task of creating the Soviet's first ICBM. Heading the OKB-1, an aeronautical design bureau, Korolev and a team of the country's finest engineers - including engineer and aeronautical designer Mikhail Tikhonravov - began work on achieving the seemingly unachievable. Taking inspiration from the German V-2, Korolev developed the R-7 rocket, a 267-ton liquid-fuelled missile capable of around 396.9 tons of thrust. Stemming from the fruits of several versions, the R-7 promised to be the first rocket to see space. Now with a method of delivery, attention turned to the satellite itself.

By January 1956 Korolev's vision for the creation of a satellite had been approved by the Soviet Presidium of the Central Committee. Originally constructed under the code name 'Object D', this new form of technology was limited to a weight of between 1,000 to 1,400 kilograms to allow its journey aboard the R-7 rocket, sitting at the head. Several versions of

Object D were designed, equipped with the latest in observational technologies. Object D housed receivers and transmitters to transmit measurements and data to stations back on Earth. Aviation technologies were incorporated in order to study areas such as the Earth's gravitational field, shape, ionosphere and space radiation, to name just a few. However, due to the IGY set by the United States, the predicted completion and launch of Object D crossed the window of opportunity, and so a simpler spherical alternative was considered.

'Prosteishy sputnik', or 'simplest satellite', became the Soviets' stand-in satellite. Simplified in size, weight and equipment, the Sputnik satellite, also known as PS, was designed to be completed and launched by the end of 1957. Only 83.6 kilograms in weight and 59 centimetres (23 inches) in diameter, the first Sputnik satellite was made by fusing two aluminium hemispheres only two millimetres thick.

Polished to perfection for easy detection, the futurist sphere extended two long antennae, finalising its now-unmistakable appearance. A technological downgrade from its predecessor, Object D, housed in the sphere was a simple radio beacon for telemetry back down to Earth. This simplistic design allowed the Soviet engineers to create a functional satellite well within the window of the IGY deadline. On 4 October 1957 at a Soviet Union testing facility in the Kazakh Republic, history was made with the launch of the Sputnik satellite. Partnered with the R-7 rocket, the elliptical sphere thrust into the atmosphere until escaping the skies into space.

After the rocket successfully escaped the atmosphere, Korolev and his team waited anxiously, ears pointed at the radio receiver. After a few moments, simple beeps sounded from the radio and cut through the tension that filled the air. Signalling the satellite's success, the beeps lasted for around two

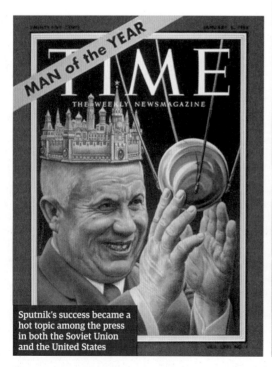

Sputnik's success became a hot topic among the press in both the Soviet Union and the United States

President of the United States, Dwight Eisenhower, announced in 1955 the US' intention to launch the world's first satellite

The third generation of Sputnik satellites was launched in 1960 to study the Earth's magnetic field

"On 4 October 1957 at a Soviet Union testing facility in the Kazakh Republic, history was made"

minutes before losing signal as Sputnik continued on its journey around the Earth. As those first few beeps came through the airwaves, the Soviet Union had secured its place as the leader in space exploration to the world. Met with roaring applause by the Soviet Union, these simple beeps signified not only the satellite's safe arrival into space, but the satellite's position in orbit, mapping the world. Travelling at around 30,000 kilometres (18,641 miles) per hour, Sputnik took 96 minutes to orbit the Earth, lasting three months before burning up on re-entry.

Sputnik mania swept the USSR. Commemorative stamps and even toys of the satellite's journey were made to celebrate its success. This venture into space had awakened the world to the power of the Soviet Union, who now saw themselves as the rightful pioneers of space. Korolev was once quoted as saying: "The Soviet Union has become the seacoast of the universe".

The once-unthinkable feat of reaching for the stars was now a reality. However, the achievement wasn't seen by all as a testament to mankind, but a threat to their freedom. The announcement of Sputnik's short-lived survival in space was initially met with congratulations in the US by President Eisenhower. However, messages of goodwill soon shifted into frenzied panic at the potential military threat to their nation, commonly known as the Sputnik crisis. Though it is believed that President Eisenhower and the US government were aware of the Sputnik satellite prior to its launch, the impact it would have on the world was greatly underestimated. What hit the American people was fear. Fear that the Soviet Union may have weaponised space. Fear that America had fallen behind as the world's technological authority they had once been held as. Such a small, insignificant satellite (especially when compared to modern-day creations) had sent a world power into utter disbelief, and fuelled the fire of its space programme. And so the Space Race had officially begun.

The United States achieved its venture into space in January 1958, launching Explorer I. Again, however, the achievement was overshadowed by the success of Sputnik 2, which delivered a dog into space only a few months after the launch of the first Sputnik. Though Sputnik had initially sparked outrage throughout the United States, as a result of its success one of the world's most respected and advanced organisations was born. Fuelled by the fire to regain their technological authority, American officials created the Advanced Research Projects Agency (later renamed DARPA), and in October 1958 the National Aeronautics and Space Administration (NASA) was created to further the work of the National Advisory Committee for Aeronautics, founded in 1915.

The two nations battled it out during the years that followed, with the Soviet Union claiming the record of putting the first man into space and woman into space. Though born from the battlefield, Sputnik's creation was a feat of not only rocket engineering, but that of scientific investigation. It sparked an era of discovery and exploration like no other. Arguably the mascot of the Space Race, Sputnik will forever be seen as a beacon of possibility.

Signalling its survival in space, Sputnik's beeps could be heard on a regular radio, allowing not only the Soviet Union to listen in...

'Flopnik'

Although achieving success in space in 1958, the United States' Explorer I satellite was not its first attempt at reaching the stars

Invigorated by Sputnik's success, America's own artificial satellite, the Vanguard, promised a more advanced analytical prowess to collect data from space. As a counterpart to Sputnik, though behind in the Space Race, Vanguard was set to launch in December of 1957. The long-awaited and highly publicised satellite was America's attempt to regain confidence in the country's ability to rival the Soviet Union. Similar in size and shape to Sputnik, the officially titled 'Naval Research Laboratory Vanguard TV3' (Test Vehicle 3) utilised a three-stage Vanguard rocket and was said to be capable of studying the effects of space's environment on the satellite, and the ability to take geodetic measurements of Earth.

However, Vanguard's journey to outer space was cut short. Launching from Florida's Cape Canaveral, the satellite and accompanying rocket only made it just over one metre off the ground before tragedy struck. Unfortunately, due to a fuel tank failure, the rocket and its satellite passenger crashed back down to the ground in a spectacular explosion. It is still unknown as to the exact cause of the rocket's misfortune, though there was speculation burning fuel had entered the fuel system before propellent pressure had been achieved. During the height of the Cold War, this was yet another blow to the US' confidence in its space abilities, with press dubbing the satellite 'Flopnik'. The failure was not long-lived, however, and by the following March of 1958, the next-generation Vanguard 1 made a successful trip into space.

Flames engulfed the fuel tanks of the Vanguard rocket, causing a massive explosion during launch

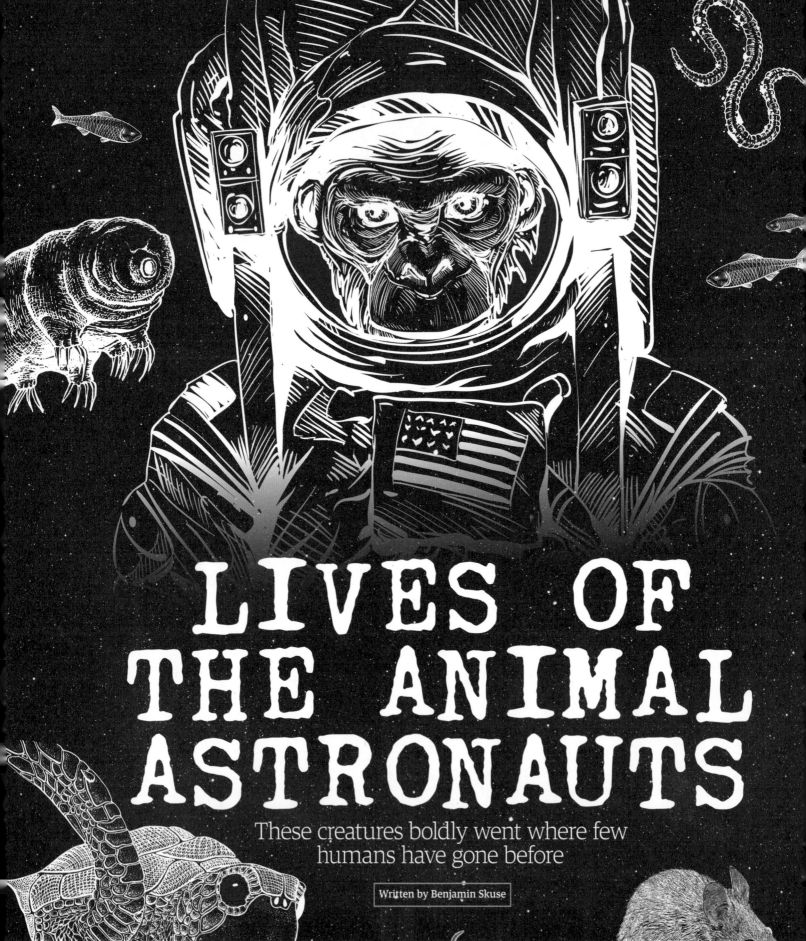

LIVES OF THE ANIMAL ASTRONAUTS

These creatures boldly went where few humans have gone before

Written by Benjamin Skuse

Muttnik orbits Earth

Perished

In the mid-20th century, the USSR launched dozens of hardy stray dogs above Earth's atmosphere to test whether humans could handle the rigours of space. The most famous of these is Laika - the first living creature to go into orbit. Captured wandering the streets of Moscow, Laika - which means 'Barker' in Russian - was strapped into a tiny space dog safety module and launched aboard Sputnik 2. Though Soviet scientists never intended Laika to return to Earth alive, at the time they suggested she had survived in space for between four days and a week before dying peacefully. It was later revealed in 2002 that her demise had been rather more harrowing. Laika had died from overheating and panic no more than seven hours after the mission began because a fan had failed. Her capsule orbited Earth 2,570 times before burning up in the atmosphere five months after blast off. In August 1960 a canine pair named Belka, or 'Squirrel', and Strelka, or 'Little Arrow' - joined by a rabbit, 42 mice and two rats - were strapped into Sputnik 5. These animals came to a less grisly end, launching into space and safely returning unharmed. Eight months later cosmonaut Yuri Gagarin famously followed in their pawsteps. Strelka went on to have six puppies, one of which - named Pushinka, or 'Fluffy' - was given to US president John F. Kennedy in 1961 by Soviet premier Nikita Khrushchev. Pushinka had four puppies with one of Kennedy's dogs, which the president affectionately referred to as pupniks.

3 November 1957/162 days

Laika the dog was the first living creature to orbit the Earth

© Sovfoto / Getty

Enos' agonising spaceflight

Survived

Enos was not the first primate in space - that accolade went to Ham earlier in 1961. He was not even the first hominid to orbit the Earth, also pipped to that distinction in 1961 by cosmonauts Yuri Gagarin and Gherman Titov. His spaceflight was simply intended to test equipment and procedures before risking a NASA astronaut. Enos' 1,263 hours of training for the flight included 'avoidance conditioning', during which electric shocks were administered to the soles of his feet if he responded incorrectly to simple tasks. This training aimed to get Enos to pull one of three levers in order to pick the odd one out from three presented shapes. In space, Enos began well during his first battery of tests. However, at the start of the second, the central lever malfunctioned. As a result, Enos was subjected to 76 unwarranted shocks. During the second orbit of an intended three, the flight encountered further problems. Alongside faulty equipment causing Enos' body temperature to rise, a stuck thruster was haemorrhaging fuel. This prompted NASA to terminate the flight early. Though an uneventful re-entry and landing, the stuck thruster caused the capsule to touch down hundreds of kilometres from where it should have. This meant Enos was stuck inside for 3 hours and 20 minutes. By the time he was extracted, Enos had broken through the protective belly panel, stripped off most of his physiological sensors and had forcibly and undoubtedly painfully removed his catheter while the balloon was still inflated. A little less than a year later, Enos died of dysentery - a sad end to an unlucky space chimp.

29 November 1961/3 hours

Enos the chimpanzee being prepared for his fateful mission that orbited Earth twice in a Mercury spacecraft

The one and only space cat

Survived

A stray cat plucked from the streets of Paris became the first and only feline sent into space. The French had previously launched three rats into space and wanted to upgrade to larger mammals to study how they responded to weightlessness. To this end, researchers captured 14 cats to train for the journey into space. These would-be feline astronauts were subjected to surgery to implant electrodes in their brains, and testing which included compression chambers and centrifuges. In the end Félicette – a petite tuxedo cat – was chosen for the mission - she was not a late replacement for a male cat called Felix who had escaped, as has been widely misreported. Aboard a Véronique AGI sounding rocket launched from a base in the Sahara Desert, she flew 157 kilometres (97.5 miles) above Earth and spent several minutes in zero gravity, all while scientists monitored her progress via the electrodes implanted in her brain. Félicette survived her trip to space and her return to Earth. Sadly, after living for two to three months back on Earth, she was put down so her brain could be studied. A second and final feline was launched towards space less than two weeks later, but that rocket failed on takeoff, leading to the loss of its furry crew. Thanks to a Kickstarter campaign raising about £43,000 ($57,000), Félicette was recently commemorated when a bronze statue honouring the one and only space cat was unveiled at the International Space University in Strasbourg, France.

© Hulton Deutsch / Getty

Félicette is the one and only feline to have ever successfully ventured into space

18 October 1963 / 13 minutes

> **"A stray cat from the streets of Paris became the first and only feline sent into space"**

Slow and steady wins the race

Survived

Bringing new meaning to Aesop's fable of *The Tortoise and the Hare*, in the race to the Moon between the US and USSR, it was two steppe tortoises who pipped the Apollo 8 crew in being the first vertebrates to successfully journey around our lunar companion. Launching from a modified Soyuz capsule in southern Kazakhstan, the unnamed tortoises - joined by mealworms, wine flies, plants, seeds, bacteria and other life, plus a 70 kilogram mannequin containing radiation detectors in the pilot's seat - were sent on a circumlunar trajectory, looping around the Moon but not orbiting it. During this time the Zond 5 spacecraft reached a closest distance of 1,950 kilometres (1,212 miles) from the Moon and took high-quality photographs of the Earth at a distance of 90,000 kilometres (55,920 miles). All occupants survived their trip, splashing down in the Indian Ocean on 21 September. Upon assessment back on land, Soviet scientists reported that the tortoises had lost ten per cent of their body weight but otherwise seemed to be in good health, remaining active and showing no loss of appetite. Later half-shelled space pioneers include tortoises launched aboard Soyuz 20 on 17 November 1975. These tortoises set the record for the longest time any animal has spent outside Earth's atmosphere - 90.5 days.

14 September 1968 / 6.5 days

Two tortoises pipped the Apollo 8 crew in being the first vertebrates to reach the Moon

The last lunar venturers

Four survived, one perished

Even at the time Apollo 17 was a poignant mission, concluding the Apollo program and so signalling an end to human travel to the Moon for the foreseeable future. Yet the smallest occupants on the mission offered hope that humanity would soon be venturing even further afield, to Mars. This was because they had been implanted with radiation monitors under their scalps to study the effects of cosmic rays during long space travel. One of the animals died during the mission for unknown reasons, but the other four remained alive, circling around the Moon a record of 75 times in 147 hours and 43 minutes with astronaut Ron Evans, while Eugene Cernan and Harrison Schmitt were conducting the last moonwalks below. After their return to Earth the four remaining live mice were killed and dissected,

and although lesions in the scalp and liver were detected they appeared to be unrelated to one another, and were not thought to be the result of cosmic rays. Furthermore, no significant damage was found to the mice's brains, eye retinas or other organs. Though inconclusive, scientists still learned a valuable lesson from the rodent experiment - that cosmic-ray experiments in particle accelerators on Earth could be useful, as they offered similar results to much more difficult space experiments. As a result, significant progress in radiobiology has been made in recent decades towards understanding the effects of cosmic rays on humans for future Mars missions.

7 December 1972/12.5 days

© NASA

The last three humans to visit the Moon were joined by five pocket mice held in tiny tubes

A student conceived the experiment that saw two orb-weaving spiders being sent to SkyLab

28 July 1973/59 days

Weaving a web of knowledge

Both perished

High-school student Judith Miles was the spark that led to the first spidernauts lifting off from Earth. She proposed an experiment to NASA called 'Web Formation in Zero Gravity', in which spiders would be released into a box where cameras would record their actions to assess how well they adapted to the absence of gravity. It was known that the geometrical structure of the web of an orb-weaving spider provides a good measure of the condition of its central nervous system. And it was thought that since spiders sense their own weight to judge how thick to weave their web, and use both the wind and gravity to sense when to begin construction, the lack of gravity in space would pose some serious issues for the arachnids. NASA agreed to the idea, and in 1973 two garden spiders called Anita and Arabella along with the experimental apparatus flew aboard the Skylab 3 mission. Though their initial efforts were distinctly confused, both spiders managed to spin sensible webs by the end of the mission, even though they were slightly finer than on Earth. Though they both died from dehydration during their flight, Anita and Arabella are preserved at the Smithsonian Air and Space Museum in Washington, DC. More recently, in 2008 and 2011, orb-weaver spiders were selected for further web-spinning experiments aboard the International Space Station (ISS), and a red-back jumping spider named Nefertiti was sent to see if it could still hunt effectively in zero gravity. All spiders showed remarkable adaptability.

23 October 2012/60 days

© JAXA

Space swimmers

Perished

Medaka - also known as Japanese rice fish - are ideal for laboratory experiments. Not only hardy and simple to rear, they also have transparent skin, making it easier for researchers to see what is going on inside their bodies. They have been a popular choice for marine experiments in space - carrying the distinction of having been the first vertebrate to successfully mate in orbit, with fry hatching on the Space Shuttle Columbia in 1994. When JAXA - the Japanese space agency - wanted to conduct an experiment to see how fish would respond to radiation impact, bone degradation and muscle wastage, medaka were the natural choice. The medaka reached the ISS in 2012, and were transferred to the station's Aquatic Habitat, a purpose-built aquarium with an automatic feeding system, water circulation system and LED lights to represent day and night. Results from this and subsequent experiments have been interesting. For humans it takes at least ten days for any space-related bone symptoms to be revealed, but the medaka started losing bone density almost immediately when they arrived in orbit. Scientists hope these experiments will shed light on the processes that govern how human bodies adapt to space as well as give new insights into bone-related human diseases like osteoporosis.

Animal milestones

Fruit flies
20 February 1947
The first animals in space were fruit flies launched on a captured Nazi V-2 rocket to a height of 109 kilometres (68 miles).

Ham
31 January 1961
Ham the chimp was the first hominid to be sent into space. He proved organisms could operate successfully in microgravity.

Albert II
14 June 1949
The first monkey in space was the American Albert II, launching to a height of 134 kilometres (83 miles).

Arabella and Anita
28 July 1973
These two spiders demonstrated that they could spin webs even in microgravity.

© Getty

Laika
3 November 1957
This Soviet space dog, dubbed 'Muttnik', was the first animal to orbit the Earth, but sadly died just hours into the mission.

Yuri Gagarin
12 April 1961
The first human in space was Yuri Gagarin, who orbited the Earth once.

Tortoises
14 September 1968
The first animals to circle the Moon were two tortoises aboard Zond 5, along with other smaller organisms.

Number of notable creatures launched into space

Figures are calculated based on best available information

 32

 25

2

I

560*

Félicette
18 October 1963
French scientists successfully launched the first cat into space in 1963.

Credit: Wikipedia, Commons Public Domain

*Correct at time of going to print

1940   1950   1960   1970

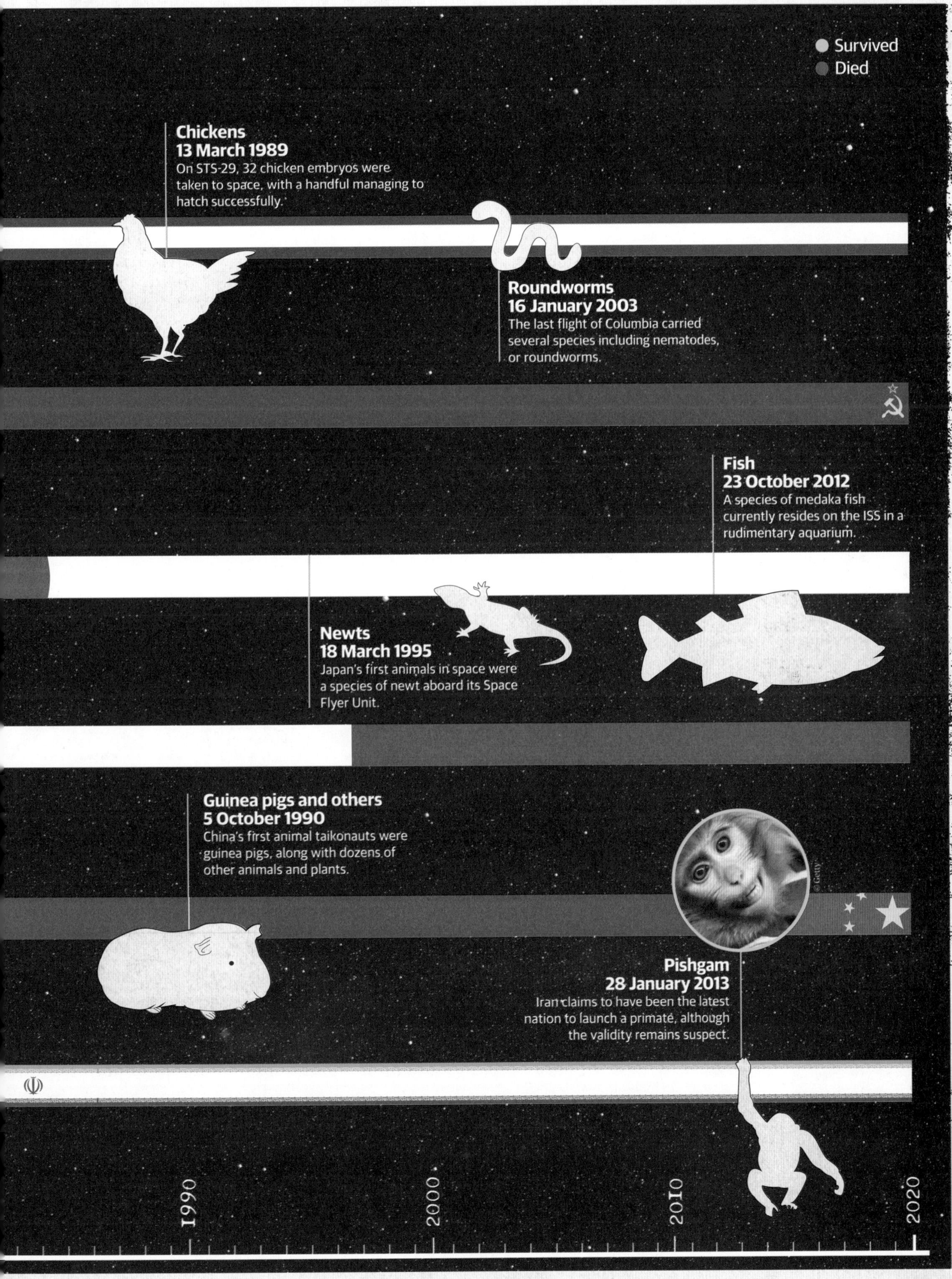

● Survived
● Died

**Chickens
13 March 1989**
On STS-29, 32 chicken embryos were taken to space, with a handful managing to hatch successfully.

**Roundworms
16 January 2003**
The last flight of Columbia carried several species including nematodes, or roundworms.

**Fish
23 October 2012**
A species of medaka fish currently resides on the ISS in a rudimentary aquarium.

**Newts
18 March 1995**
Japan's first animals in space were a species of newt aboard its Space Flyer Unit.

**Guinea pigs and others
5 October 1990**
China's first animal taikonauts were guinea pigs, along with dozens of other animals and plants.

© Getty

**Pishgam
28 January 2013**
Iran claims to have been the latest nation to launch a primate, although the validity remains suspect.

1990

2000

2010

2020

Amphibian balancing act

Both perished

Two very different space adventurers were ready to spring into action in 1970, all in the name of understanding the effects of space travel and weightlessness on humans. The Orbiting Frog Otolith – 'otolith' refers to the frogs' inner-ear balance mechanism – spacecraft contained two bullfrogs that were in for a wild ride. After having surgery to implant electrodes into their thoraxes and vestibular systems – a part of the nervous system within the inner ear that helps to maintain balance – the frogs' nerves connecting their limb muscles were cut to prevent them from accidentally removing the electrodes. They were then placed in water for the duration of the flight to cushion them from vibrations and to keep them cool. Interestingly, after a bumpy first few days, by the last day of the six-day flight the frogs' vestibular systems had returned to normal, suggesting that they acclimatised to their space environment. Unfortunately for the frogs, they never returned to Earth. Many other frogs have been launched both before and after the Orbiting Frog Otolith experiment in the name of science.

©NASA

9 November 1970/6 days

A tragedy's only survivors

16 January 2003/16 days

© NASA

Survived

The Space Shuttle Columbia had served for roughly 22 years, completing 27 missions before its 2003 flight. On this fateful last mission, launch and orbit appeared to go well. However, the spacecraft and its seven-astronaut crew were tragically lost on re-entry to Earth's atmosphere. Caused by a hole that had been punctured in one of Columbia's wings during takeoff 16 days earlier, the disaster ultimately ended the Space Shuttle program. The initial seven-month investigation of the Columbia disaster yielded nearly 85,000 pieces of the spacecraft, including many of the 60 science experiments, some of which involved animals. Of the fish, insects, spiders, bees and silk worms that had been aboard, only the nematode worms survived.

Hundreds of microscopic nematodes were found inside Petri dishes held in six canisters within a four-kilogram locker. It was the locker's robustness, reinforced specifically to protect the materials inside, that saved the nematodes. Yet the worms found were not the original survivors. As nematodes have a life cycle of seven to ten days, by the time they were discovered the worms were fourth- or fifth-generation descendants of the original spacefarers. From the amazing survival of the nematodes, astrobiologists learned that life can potentially travel between planets by natural means.

"Life can potentially travel between planets"

Hardiest animal on Earth, and in space

14 September 2007/12 days

Survived

If you found a tardigrade floating in space, you would assume it was alien. Less than one-millimetre long, tardigrades are short, plump and puffy creatures, with four pairs of legs that each end in claws or sucking discs, and a tubular mouth ringed by teeth-like structures called stylets. Commonly known as 'water bears' or 'moss piglets', they are found in almost every environment imaginable on Earth, and are remarkably hardy. For this reason, in 2007 three groups of tardigrades were sent into space on the European Space Agency's Foton-M3 mission. The first group were exposed to the vacuum of outer space, the second group vacuum plus an unhealthy dose of solar radiation and the third vacuum plus full solar radiation exposure. Staggeringly, when returned to Earth and rehydrated, the first group showed no signs of damage. The two groups exposed to solar radiation fared worse, but even in the group exposed to a full dose of solar radiation, three tardigrades were successfully reanimated. It is for this reason some people believe tardigrades are alive on the Moon – in April 2019, Israeli spacecraft Beresheet crash-landed on the Moon carrying thousands of the tiny creatures.

Tardigrades are indisputably the hardiest creatures on Earth and in space

Source: Wikipedia commons
© Nicole Ottawa & Oliver Meckes / Eye of Science

EVERYTHING YOU NEED TO KNOW ABOUT A UNIVERSAL ENIGMA

Whether they're supermassive, primordial or double, black holes are a mystery. It's time to strip away some of puzzle as we head inside black holes to find out how they work and what really happens on the event horizon.

The beginning of NASA: Project Mercury

Project Mercury was the first major project NASA embarked on, as the Space Race with the Soviets intensified

The start of NASA's longstanding presence in space began with Project Mercury. Without this project, the Apollo missions that took mankind to the Moon never would have happened. On 7 October 1958, when NASA was only a few months old, Project Mercury was officially unveiled as NASA's first major project. It had three very clear aims as the US went head-to-head with the Soviet Union in the Space Race. First, NASA wanted to be able to place a human in orbit around Earth successfully; second, they wanted to understand how space flight affects the human body, and last they wanted to be able to return both the astronaut and space vessel safely back to Earth.

Before NASA could send anyone to space, the team of America's first future astronauts had to be found and the Mercury space capsule had to be designed and brought into existence. The Mercury space capsule was only big enough to fit a single person inside, but it had everything in it for one to survive and was an engineering masterpiece at the time. The cone-shaped capsule had a series of parachutes, boosters, vital supplies (e.g. water, oxygen etc), an antenna, a heatshield and a room that would accommodate the astronaut on their journey and ensure a safe return back to the surface.

But who was to going to fill these capsules? On 9 April 1959, the NASA administrator under President Eisenhower, Thomas Keith Glennan, announced the seven pioneers that would battle it out against the Soviets in a press conference in Washington DC, United States. Malcolm Scott Carpenter, Leroy Gordon Cooper Jr, John Herschel Glenn Jr, Virgil Ivan (Gus) Grissom, Walter Marty Schirra Jr, Alan Bartlett Shepard Jr and Donald Kent Slayton were the chosen soldiers and were henceforth known as 'Mercury Seven'. The selection process for these astronauts was extremely strict as the NASA committee in charge of astronaut selection were well aware of the unusual conditions of spaceflight. The committee decided to single out military test pilots who thrived in high-performance aircraft and had shown as much with a lot of flying experience, a piece of criteria that excluded the likes of Neil Armstrong, the first man to step on the Moon as part of Apollo 11. After a series of extreme physical, psychological and mental examinations, 110 candidates were narrowed down to these seven. Within the rejected 103 were people that would later successfully go through Gemini and Apollo missions, but in this instance, they couldn't make the cut. These figures included the likes of Jim Lovell of Apollo 8, who didn't pass the medical tests, and Pete Conrad, who was the third man to walk on the Moon as part of Apollo 12, and who didn't want to endure any more invasive medical tests. The Mercury Seven men went on to have distinguished careers with NASA, but at the time they immediately shot to fame. The heady combination of the fact that the United States was in an intense space race, and tales of the exotic training and experiences that lay ahead for these astronauts, saw public interest in these men reach a new height.

The training that the Mercury Seven underwent shaped the procedures that would later have a heavy influence on the Apollo mission. This training program was split into five major categories consisting of basic astronautical science instruction,

President Kennedy toured NASA's Cape Canaveral site several times. The Launch Operations Center was renamed the John F Kennedy Space Center after his death

A Marine helicopter picks up Mercury astronaut Alan Shepard and his Freedom 7 capsule

"Alan Shepard became the first American in space after completing a historic 15-minute sub-orbital flight"

systems training, spacecraft control training, environmental familiarisation, and egress and survival training. The tests that the Mercury Seven crew underwent were also taken by 13 women behind closed doors, and led by William Randolph Lovelace, who was the chairman of NASA's Special Advisory Committee on Life Science. This privately-funded programme showed that these women could not only pass the tests the Mercury Seven crew went through, but some even surpassed their male rivals. However, NASA's requirement that would-be astronauts be highly qualified jet pilots automatically excluded them from participation in the fledgling space programme. The First Lady Astronaut Trainees, or the Mercury 13 as they were later dubbed, began a fight for woman's rights and against prejudice and discrimination, which they eventually won. The Soviet space programme, however, put the first woman into space in 1963. An American woman would not go up until 20 years later.

In order to test the Mercury space capsules as well as the two launch vehicles that were going to take the first Americans into space, Atlas and Redstone, NASA performed unmanned missions; some empty and some containing animals. These valiant creatures include the likes of a rhesus monkey named Sam, and two chimpanzees named Ham and Enos. The Mercury-Redstone rocket was designed to take humans to a sub-orbital flight, whereas the Atlas rocket would put humans into a low-Earth orbit.

On the 5 May 1961, 23 days after Russian cosmonaut Yuri Gagarin became the first person in space after a 108-minute flight, Alan Shepard became the first American in space after completing a historic 15-minute sub-orbital flight in space as part of the Freedom 7 mission. Shepard also went on to be the spacecraft commander of Apollo 14, and became the fifth man to walk on the Moon. This mission was repeated on 21 July 1961 so that NASA could again study and improve human spaceflight. Gus Grissom flew the Liberty Bell 7 mission, which saw two changes to the previous space capsule. This capsule had an explosively actuated side hatch and a viewing

mirror, as requested by the Mercury astronauts. After another 15 minutes in space, the Liberty Bell 7 hatch blew out early and Grissom hit the Atlantic Ocean, with water quickly flooding the vessel. For a moment, Grissom almost drowned, but he managed to escape Liberty Bell 7 and was rescued after only a few minutes of being out in the ocean. Unfortunately, Grissom was one of the unlucky three people that later perished in a flash fire during Apollo 1 tests.

After the Redstone missions had been completed, the United States was still playing catch-up with the Soviet Union as they had more people in space and had logged more time in space at this point. The first manned spaceflight of the Atlas launch vehicle was on 20 February 1962, with John Glenn riding in the Friendship 7 spacecraft. This mission lasted for

almost five hours in space, travelling at an altitude of 260 kilometres (162 miles), thus making Glenn the first American to orbit the Earth, which he did three times. Glenn had a very interesting career post-Mercury, as after he left NASA, he became a US Senator and then later returned to NASA in 1998 to become the oldest person to ever fly in space at the age of 77 as part of the STS-95 crew.

The Project Mercury flights that took place after this were performed purely as research operations, in order to push the boundaries of human space flight and understand how it affects the human body. On 24 May of the same year, Carpenter had his turn to fly in space. Aurora 7, as it was named, was a replicated mission that covered an equal time in space and simply confirmed the success of Friendship 7. This mission should have been Slayton's turn, however a couple of months before the launch he was ruled out on the grounds of a medical condition called idiopathic atrial fibrillation, which meant he had an erratic heart rate. Slayton still went on to have a great career as

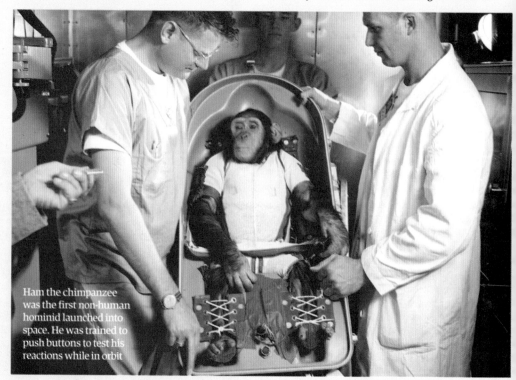

Ham the chimpanzee was the first non-human hominid launched into space. He was trained to push buttons to test his reactions while in orbit

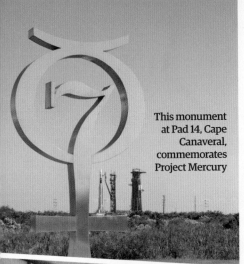

This monument at Pad 14, Cape Canaveral, commemorates Project Mercury

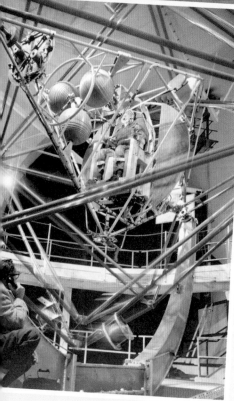

The history of Project Mercury

The insignias from the six manned missions and the signatures of the seven Mercury Seven crewmembers surround the United States' first spacecraft, the Mercury spacecraft. These six missions had times in space that started at just 15 minutes and finished with an astonishing 34-hour mission, completing 22 orbits of Earth.

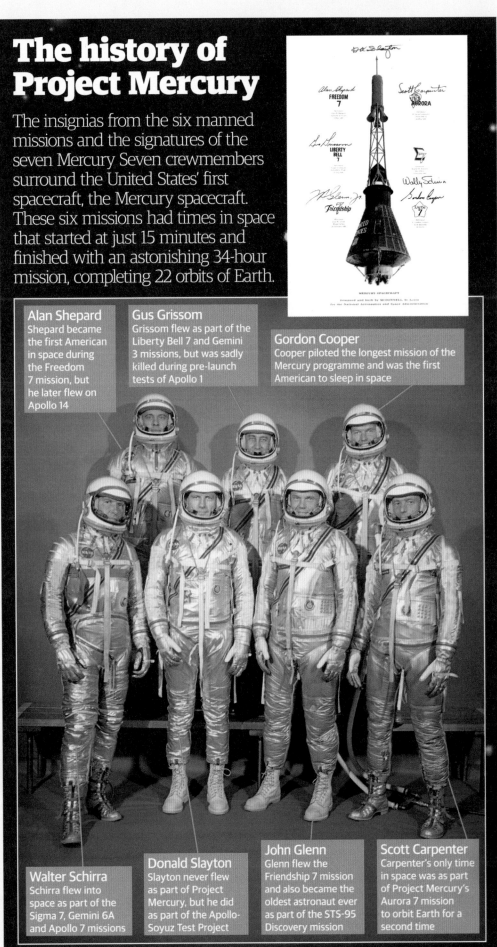

Alan Shepard
Shepard became the first American in space during the Freedom 7 mission, but he later flew on Apollo 14

Gus Grissom
Grissom flew as part of the Liberty Bell 7 and Gemini 3 missions, but was sadly killed during pre-launch tests of Apollo 1

Gordon Cooper
Cooper piloted the longest mission of the Mercury programme and was the first American to sleep in space

Walter Schirra
Schirra flew into space as part of the Sigma 7, Gemini 6A and Apollo 7 missions

Donald Slayton
Slayton never flew as part of Project Mercury, but he did as part of the Apollo-Soyuz Test Project

John Glenn
Glenn flew the Friendship 7 mission and also became the oldest astronaut ever as part of the STS-95 Discovery mission

Scott Carpenter
Carpenter's only time in space was as part of Project Mercury's Aurora 7 mission to orbit Earth for a second time

an astronaut, participating in the Apollo-Soyuz test project that marked the end of the Space Race.

On 12 September, John F Kennedy made his famous speech that stated the United States was heading for the Moon. So from then on, Project Mercury was all about increasing the intensity of spaceflight and seeing how long an astronaut could stay in space for, which helped the preparation for a mission to the Moon. Sigma 7 was undertaken by Schirra on 3 October; he spent a total of nine hours in space and orbited the Earth six times. This was a good indicator that the United States was moving in the right direction. The last mission, the mission that would close the curtain on the outstanding Project Mercury, was undertaken by Cooper on board the Faith 7 space vessel. Cooper spent 34 hours in space so that scientists could evaluate the effects of over a whole day in space, a time that seemed inconceivable at the time of Shepard's flight. Both Cooper and Schirra went on to be heavily involved in Project Gemini, and Schirra even went on to be commander of Apollo 7. The collective efforts of everyone involved with Project Mercury were fundamental to humanity exploring the next frontier, the Moon, and Project Mercury was followed swiftly by Project Gemini, which was formally conceived in January 1962.

Mercury-Redstone 3 is launched with its pilot Alan Shepard, on a suborbital mission to place the first American in space

Alan Shepard
the first American in space

The Mercury 7 astronaut who made history, paving the way for the US' Space Race success

Written by Baljeet Panesar

The launch of Sputnik 1 by the Soviet Union on 4 October 1957 came as a huge surprise to America – a worrying indication that the Soviet Union had exceeded the technological capabilities of the US. Then, on 12 September 1959, the Soviets launched Luna 2 – the first spacecraft to land on the Moon, heralding another step forward in the Soviet's space programme. In response to the Luna programme, the US established the Ranger program in 1959. However, the first successful Ranger craft, Ranger 7, would not impact the Moon until some five years later.

Given the threat posed by the Soviets, in 1959 the newly formed NASA invited 110 test flight pilots to volunteer for the US' first manned spaceflight programme, called Project Mercury. The Mercury program had been officially approved on 7 October 1958, and its aim was to successfully place a man into Earth orbit and return him safety – preferably before the Soviets. From a shortlist of 32 candidates, NASA administrator T. Keith Glennan announced the first seven – the Mercury 7, as they were known – on

9 April 1959 after a two-month selection process. They were Alan B. Shepard, John H. Glenn, Virgil "Gus" I. Grissom, Donald 'Deke' K. Slayton, Malcolm 'Scott' S. Carpenter, Walter "Wally" M. Schirra and L. Gordon Cooper. From these seven, it would be Shepard who would be selected to pilot the US' inaugural flight into space.

The Mercury program consisted of six manned flights between 1961 and 1963 – two suborbital missions and four that orbited the Earth. The total flight time for these manned missions was 53 hours, 55 minutes and 27 seconds, but the programme also included some 20 developmental flights. The Mercury program was successfully completed on 16 May 1961 after Gordon Cooper completed a 22-orbit flight in his spacecraft Faith 7. Over the five years of Project Mercury NASA proved that they could place a man in orbit, that he could survive in space and that he and the spacecraft were able to return safely back to Earth.

But before NASA launched men into space, the Mercury spacecraft were tested by launching

On 29 April 1961, Shepard undertakes a flight simulation test in preparation for the history-making flight

"The Mercury program's aim was to successfully place a man into Earth orbit and return him safety"

A life's work

America's first man in space would also become the fifth man to walk on the Moon

After graduating from high school, Shepard attended the United States Naval Academy graduating in 1944. He began his naval career on destroyer USS Cogswell in the Pacific Ocean towards the end of World War II. He subsequently completed his flight training at Naval Air Station Corpus Christi, Texas, and Naval Air Station Pensacola, Florida, and received his naval wings in 1947.

In 1950 he attended the United States Test Pilot School in Maryland, where he conducted high-altitude tests for various aircraft and in-flight refuelling systems. He also tested aircraft landings on the first angled carrier deck. He qualified as a test pilot in 1951, and would continue in this role during the 1950s. Shepard would later return as a test pilot and perform test flights with the F3H Demon and F-8 Crusader, as well as acting as project test pilot for the F5D Skylancer. Eventually Shepard became an instructor in the Test Pilot School, logging more than 8,000 hours of flying time, of which 3,700 hours were in jet aircraft.

Shepard was scheduled to command the first manned Gemini mission, but he was grounded after being diagnosed with Ménière's disease, an inner ear disorder which affects hearing and balance. However, years later he would undergo surgery which would allow him to fly once again.

In January and February 1971 Shepard acted as commander of the Apollo 14 mission, becoming the fifth man to walk on the Moon – the only Mercury astronaut to do so. During this mission Shepard

became the first – and only – person to hit a golf ball on another celestial body outside of Earth. This science experiment demonstrated how objects behave in the Moon's lower gravity. Over his two spaceflights Shepard logged a total of 216 hours and 57 minutes in space, of which nine hours and 17 minutes were spent on a lunar extravehicular activity.

On 5 May 1961, Shepard made a 15-minute suborbital flight, securing him the accolade of the first American in space

During the 33 hours that Shepard (pictured) and Mitchell were on the Moon, they completed two moonwalks totalling over nine hours

Ancient Earth rock found on the Moon

The 4-billion-year-old Earth rock that was brought back to Earth

Shepard would later command the Apollo 14 mission, with Stuart A. Rossa as the Command Module pilot and Edgar D. Mitchell as the Lunar Module pilot. The mission was the third to land on the Moon and the eighth manned mission of the Apollo program, landing in the Fra Mauro region. The crew conducted geological and seismic experiments.

On 6 February 1971 the crew collected some 42 kilograms (93 pounds) of Moon rock that was brought back to Earth. Almost 50 years later it was discovered one of these Moon rocks – a nine-kilogram (20-pound) sample formally named 14321 – may have been formed between 4 and 4.1 billion years ago, about 20 kilometres (12.4 miles) beneath the surface of the Earth. The early Solar System was a violent place where Earth was repeatedly hit by asteroids. It's thought that one of these impacts launched the rock towards the Moon, where it partially melted 3.9 billion years ago and was once again buried. At this time the Moon was three-times closer to the Earth than it is today. It's believed another impact some 26 million years ago pushed the sample back on the lunar surface, where it remained undisturbed until Shepard collected it.

As part of an international collaboration with the Center for Lunar Science and Exploration, researchers found a two-gram (0.07 ounce) fragment composed of quartz, feldspar and zircon which were formed in a low temperature, oxygen environment – conditions commonly found on Earth, but not on the Moon. Although it is possible that the rocks could have a lunar origin, this would require specific conditions which have not previously been observed from samples. But it's possible that more bits of Earth have found their way to the Moon.

Pictured here near Cone Crater, rock 14321 was collected by Alan Shepard from the lunar surface

After a post-flight inspection, Shepard emerges from the Freedom 7 spacecraft

monkeys. The most famous is Ham the chimpanzee – the first higher primate to test a spacecraft – who was launched aboard the Mercury-Redstone 2 mission in January 1961. Although the mission was (mostly) successful and Ham returned to Earth without injury, problems with the Redstone became apparent. Consequently, NASA and its rocket engineer Wernher von Braun decided to add an additional unmanned flight in March 1961. This was a precautionary measure after a failed launch attempt in November 1960 where the rocket rose only ten centimetres (four inches) off the launch pad. This additional flight was successful, but postponed

Shepard's flight to May. The additional months ensured that the Redstone was safe for Shepard, but it provided an opportunity to the Soviets, allowing them to get even further ahead in the Space Race against the US.

After a rigorous training schedule, including a series of launch simulations, the first performed on 18 April 1961, Shepard was launched from Launch Complex 5 at Cape Canaveral Air Force Station in the Freedom 7 spacecraft aboard the 25-metre (83-foot) Mercury-Redstone 3 launch vehicle on 5 May 1961 at 09:34 EST (14:34 UTC). The formal countdown for the start of the mission started the day before, and by the time Shepard was launched he had spent more than four hours in Freedom 7, famously encouraging NASA technicians to "fix your little problem and light this candle". These delays were a result of weather conditions that prevented filming of the launch, and last-minute repairs which had to be made to the spacecraft.

The cramped Freedom 7 spacecraft only had enough room for one man, and was 3.51 metres (11.5 feet) high and 1.89 metres (6.2 feet) in diameter - smaller than the Vostok 1 spacecraft, which had a height of 4.4 metres (14.4 feet). The Redstone rockets were initially used as missiles by the US Army and were modified to allow for the launch of a manned Mercury capsule.

23 days earlier, Soviet cosmonaut Yuri Gagarin became the first person in space - the Soviet Union's second major victory over its American rivals - reaching a maximum altitude of 327 kilometres (203 miles). Shepard's original mission was scheduled for 2 May 1961, but the historic flight was delayed due to weather conditions. Unlike Gagarin, who completed a 108-minute flight that also orbited the Earth, Shepard's historic flight lasted 15 minutes and 28 seconds but did not orbit the Earth, a milestone that was achieved by John Glenn who completed three orbits of the Earth on 20 February 1962.

Freedom 7 was programmed to complete a ballistic trajectory, carrying Shepard to an altitude of 187 kilometres (116.5 miles) and reaching a maximum speed of 8,262 kilometres (5,134 miles) per hour. Using Freedom 7's periscope - the spacecraft did not have a window - and having become the first American to observe the Earth, Shepard exclaimed: "What a beautiful view!" During the flight Shepard was capable of manoeuvring Freedom 7 using hand controls to activate the spacecraft's thrusters, whereas Gagarin's flight was entirely automatic, but Gagarin had travelled at a speed of over 27,000 kilometres (17,000 miles) per hour. Having experienced forces as high as 11gs (11-times the force of gravity) during re-entry, the spacecraft's parachute was deployed, making a successful splashdown in the Atlantic some 488 kilometres (303 miles) from Cape Canaveral.

Gagarin's triumphant flight saw him eject from his spacecraft at an altitude of seven kilometres (23,000 feet) and return to Earth using a parachute, which was not disclosed at the time and remained confidential for years. Shepard and the spacecraft were recovered by helicopter and taken to the USS Lake Champlain aircraft carrier which was awaiting their arrival, and he was greeted with a hero's welcome. After a post-flight medical investigation, doctors reported that Shepard was "disgustingly normal". 20 days after Shepard's success, President John F. Kennedy committed America to landing a man on the Moon by the end of the 1960s, thereby ending the Space Race.

The success of the mission also ensured that the spacecraft and booster were closer to being certified for Earth-orbiting missions. For becoming the second person in space, Shepard received the NASA Distinguished Service Medal from President Kennedy, as well as the Distinguished Flying Cross. Following the success of Shepard's flight he was treated as a national hero, with ticker-tape parades in his honour, once again uniting Americans with a sense

Shepard receives his Distinguished Service Medal from President Kennedy on 8 May 1961

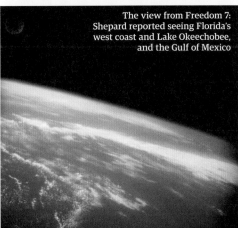

The view from Freedom 7: Shepard reported seeing Florida's west coast and Lake Okeechobee, and the Gulf of Mexico

"An estimated 45 million people watched Shepard's flight in the US"

of achievement and pride at the US' space efforts. Despite the possibility that the flight may not have been successful, it was broadcast on television and radio with an estimated 45 million people watching Shepard's historic flight in the US alone, allowing the world to watch the technological advances of a superpower. This was important given the criticism NASA had previously faced from the media and the public over the Soviet Union's progress and its initial domination of space. Although Gagarin's name was highly publicised, the history-making flight, as well as any setbacks, were not broadcast, in keeping with the secrecy in the Soviet Union.

Although the US appeared to be behind in the Space Race, Shepard's historic flight helped gain support for its space exploration programme, and allowed the American people to share the excitement, anguish and success of spaceflight with the brave and courageous men who travelled to space. The accomplishments of the Mercury program provided the foundation for the successes of the subsequent Gemini program and Apollo manned missions, and the US' eventual superiority space exploration.

Within 11 minutes of splashdown in the Atlantic Ocean, Shepard and Freedom 7 were flown to their recovery ship

Shepard entering the Freedom 7 spacecraft in his pressure suit and helmet

The Mercury 7 were NASA's first group of astronauts, selected in April 1959

INTERVIEW BIO

Wally Funk

Funk was a 22-year-old aviator when she volunteered to be part of the Women in Space Program. Having undergone the same tough, physiological screening as the astronauts who had been selected for Project Mercury, she was one of 13 who passed. She and the others suffered a major blow as funding was pulled, leaving her dream to become an astronaut in tatters.

Although she then became a Goodwill Ambassador and a flight instructor, Funk's desire to go into space has never left her.

"I don't get angry. I was disappointed. I threw it a fish"

In 1961, Wallace "Wally" Funk hoped to become one of the first women in space. Now, she's determined to embark on a journey of a lifetime aboard Virgin Galactic

When did you first become interested in space and what was it that caught your imagination?
First I was interested in flying. I jumped off the barn trying to fly when I was four years old wearing a Superman cape. Luckily I'd made sure there was a hay bale down there.

What steps did you take to become an astronaut as a teenager?
I didn't think about going into space for real until I was 21. But luckily all the things I did as a teenager were what you needed to become an astronaut. I was fit and did everything at altitude because I lived in Taos. That's where I was born and raised, in Taos, New Mexico, at 7,000 feet [2,134 metres]. I am used to altitude. I skied at 13,000 [3,962 metres].

So, as a youngster, I was able to do anything I wanted to do: bike, shoot, ride, ski. I was never told no. If I hurt myself I licked my wounds and went about my business. I was totally brought up differently from most girls. I had a Wild West costume as a child because I wanted to be a cowboy. A cowgirl. My mother got chaps for me, and boots. I had my gun and my belt, and I rode a palomino horse, Victor. I made model aeroplanes and liked space.

How did it feel to complete your first solo flight at the age of 16, and what did the aviation programme at Stephens College teach you?
When I first got to Stephens I didn't think I was going to like it. The girls had long hair and I had a short haircut. I was dressed well but I didn't fit in. They were frou-frou. About the second day, I called home and said, "I don't know if this is the right place for me." I was a tomboy. I did mostly sports. Mother spoke to my adviser and asked him if they had an airport, and Stephens had started an aviation programme in Columbia Municipal Airport. Mother told him to get Wally out there and I started flying.

I passed my solo license. It was great and I took mother up as my second or third passenger. I was thrilled and she was thrilled to go up. A dream had come true for her because she had always wanted to be a pilot, but she didn't tell me that until I was older.

I joined the Stephens Susies flight team, and in my last year I was super-qualified to go to NIFA [National Intercollegiate Flying Association] air meets in the United States. I'd have a co-pilot and she would navigate and I'd fly races and sometimes I'd win them. So it taught me how to fly and how to win races.

What drove you to volunteer to be a part of the Women in Space Program in 1961 and how important was it for you to try and become one of the first women in space?
I was working at Fort Sill military base in Oklahoma training pilots. I was a civilian and their first woman flight instructor. The year before I saw an article about Jerrie Cobb in *Life* magazine. She was a pilot, like me, and the first woman to pass the same tests as the Mercury 7 astronauts. It said she had complained less than the men had.

So I wrote to Jerrie and Dr William Randolph Lovelace – he was in charge of the tests – and volunteered as part of the Woman in Space Program. They only wanted women pilots and, same as the men, I took the astronaut tests in February 1961 in Albuquerque, New Mexico, at the Lovelace Clinic. I was the youngest to pass the tests. I was 22 years old – my parents had to sign permission for me to do them – and I excelled. In some of the tests, I beat the guys.

How gruelling were the physical and psychological tests – what were the most testing?
I swallowed three feet [0.9 metres] of rubber hose,

Wally was determined to become one of the first women in space, and she took part in rigorous training

No Man In Moon

Stephens Graduate Trains To Be Female Astronaut

Wally is ensuring she is well prepared for a trip into space by putting her body through the conditions she will experience, such as zero graviy

I had barium enemas and had to place my hands and feet in ice water for three minutes. All kinds of needles and electrodes were stuck in our bodies, not the kind that are plastered on today. They were sort of painful, but pain was not a situation with me. I would do anything. On the exercise bike test, measuring our lung capacity, you had to ride until you were exhausted.

A clock was right in front of you. It was a psychological factor, I'm sure, and you would pedal to the speed of a metronome. It was ticking, going back and forth in a room full of doctors and nurses. I wanted to break the barrier on that test and go for 11 minutes because ten was all they expected. It was pretty easy going until nine and a half, ten minutes, so I gritted my teeth, closed my eyes and felt my second wind coming, and I did it. All the electrodes were taken from me and they said, "Wally. I think we better help you." And I said, "No, I'm fine" and then I fell right down.

The worst test was when they injected ice water in your ear. It makes you go crazy and you lose control of your body. But mother said when I was four or five, when I had my horse Victor, if you fall off your bike or horse, you lick your wounds. Don't come back running home crying. They taught me to look after myself. When I was at Lovelace I took care of myself and I never complained. Only 13 of us passed these phase one tests - the same as the Mercury 7 astronauts.

You became one of the Mercury 13, yet a week before the final phase of training, the programme was cancelled: how disappointed and angry were you, and did you feel cheated?
I don't get angry. I was disappointed and I threw it a fish.

"I jumped off the barn trying to fly when I was four"

Did you consider giving up at this stage? Was there a feeling that you were facing a very unfair, uphill battle?
No. I decided to do the rest of the tests myself and find other places where I could get more testing. That's why I'm the only girl to have done all three phases of the astronaut training.

I had already taken some optional tests after phase one - psychological and evaluated stress response - with Rhea Hurrle [another member of the Mercury 13] before they'd cancelled. This was the isolation test where I stayed in an isolation tank, with water and air the same temperature as my body, in complete darkness for ten hours and 35 minutes. I beat all the guys on that one, including John Glenn. It makes most people go a little loopy, but not me.

So I decided to do all the remaining phase two and three tests by myself. I wrote to all the institutions and got in and did them. I did a centrifuge test at the University of Southern California and the Martin-Baker seat-ejection test at El Toro Marine Corps Air Station in California.

How did you feel in 1969 watching Neil Armstrong become the first to set foot on the Moon?
It was great. But there should have been a woman up there. We were ready to be astronauts. I was ready to be an astronaut and to go to the Moon.

Following the disappointment, you became a Goodwill Ambassador and America's first female aviation inspector. How much of a triumph, personally and historically, was this?
It was a great job and I loved it. After that I became an NTSB air-crash investigator, the first woman to do that too in the United States. I loved those jobs.

Despite your successes, your dream of becoming an astronaut has never wavered. How excited are you to have a place on a Virgin Galactic spaceplane? I'm thrilled but I want to go up real soon. I'm going to be sat on the right-hand side, right behind the first officer.

What are you hoping to achieve during your spaceflight, and how are you preparing for it?
I keep real fit. I do exercises every day and take some vitamins. And I go flying every weekend.

How much has changed over the years? Is it now much easier for women to become astronauts or is more work still needed?
Nowadays the girls do just as well as the guys. My friend Eileen Collins [NASA astronaut] was the first girl to pilot the Space Shuttle. She's great. I met Samantha Cristoforetti [ESA astronaut] and she flew fighter jets in the Italian airforce and speaks five languages. These women are outstanding.

Do you dream that space travel will one day be open to us all?
Absolutely.

Wally Funk's Race for Space by Sue Nelson is published by Westbourne Press

If her programme hadn't been cancelled, perhaps Funk could've been the first woman on the Moon

Funk has met Italian ESA astronaut Samantha Cristoforetti who holds the record for the longest uninterrupted spaceflight of a European, at 199 days and 16 hours

From left: The Mercury 13's Gene Nora Jessen, Wally Funk, Jerrie Cobb, Jerri Truhill, Sarah Rutley, Myrtle Cagle and Bernice Steadman

The success of Vostok 1 was an enormous propaganda victory for the Soviets, forever immortalising the cosmonaut, Yuri Gagarin

The FIRST MAN in SPACE

After a stellar start to the space race, the Soviet Vostok programme dealt the US a crushing blow

Written by Hareth Al Bustani

By the late-1950s, having kicked off the Space Race by launching Sputnik into Earth's orbit, the USSR went on to develop the first spacecraft to land on the Moon and send the first animal into orbit. With these successive victories over the US space programme, the Soviets gained legitimate ground to claim technological supremacy on the world stage.

However, while dogs and metal were one thing, the Americans were not long behind, and there was still one great defining breakthrough that neither side had yet managed to accomplish - one that would capture imaginations and thrust humans into a new epoch - sending a person into space.

The Soviets began developing systems for a manned orbital satellite in 1958. The project was led by Mikhail Tikhonravov, who had worked on rocket design and space exploration with Sergei Korolev since 1933, and chief conceptual designer Konstantin Feoktistov, a stubborn and brilliant scientist who hoped to one day visit space himself.

In April 1959 the team drew up a secret draft plan of a spacecraft capable of carrying man into space, followed the next month by ballistic calculations with orbital descent options. The army gave them access to firing ranges, military specialists, troops and, crucially, the newly updated R-7A rocket - with an added third stage capable of launching a payload of five tonnes into near-Earth orbit.

While the Americans had successfully developed the Discoverer espionage satellite which would later carry cameras and film, the Soviets still lacked the technology to bring vessels back to Earth - something essential for a manned mission. To speed things along, Premier Khrushchev tasked the Experimental Design Bureau OKB-1 with developing a satellite for reconnaissance and navigation alongside a "sputnik for human flight".

After some heated debates Korolev signed off on a ballistic landing configuration with a spherical descent module, equipped with a thermal shield. An instrument aggregate compartment housing disposable hardware would simply break off before entering the atmosphere.

As the US continued developing its own Atlas missile, capable of carrying over 1.3 tonnes into

12 АПРЕЛЯ 1961

Yuri Gagarin

How the world's first cosmonaut rose from an obscure farm to space

Yuri Alekseyevich Gagarin was born in 1934 in the village of Klushino, near Gzhatsk, a region of around 10,000 people in the heart of central Russia. His parents Aleksey and Anna were peasants, members of a collective farm, growing grain and flax.

His early life was a traditional one, growing up in a log hut with a thatched roof, set amidst fields and forests. However, Yuri's world was turned upside down when Nazi Panzer units overran the village in 1941. A Nazi officer took over the Gagarin residence during the last years of occupation.

After the war the Gagarins moved to Gzhatsk, where Aleksey worked as a carpenter, Anna tended the fields and Yuri continued his secondary education – joining the Young Communist League in 1949. He later moved to Lyubertsy, an industrial suburb of Moscow, where he fell in love with volleyball, basketball and, most importantly, aeronautics and space – never missing an airshow at the nearby Tushino Airfield.

Having graduated from vocational school as a moulder with distinction, he enrolled at an industrial college in Saratov, joining the Saratov Aero Club. After completing his studies he enlisted at a Soviet Air Force training centre, graduating in 1957 with top honours. While there he met the love of his life, Valentina, with whom he would later have two children.

The 27-year-old Yuri Gagarin emerged from the Vostok mission, not just one of 1,200 Gagarins living in Moscow, but a living legend. As Khrushchev would tell him: "You have made yourself immortal, because you are the first to penetrate into space." Named a Hero of the Soviet Union by a smooching Khrushchev, monuments of Yuri were erected across the country and streets were named in his honour.

Training future space cadets, he quickly rose up in the Communist party, chairing the Soviet-Cuban Friendship Society, attending the 22nd Congress of the Communist Party and becoming deputy in the Supreme Soviet.

Unfortunately, in 1968, having reached a colonel's rank, Gagarin died test piloting a new aircraft; a devastatingly pedestrian death for one of the USSR's most beloved heroes. Despite his untimely demise, the cosmonaut's reputation outlived that of even the Communist regime. As one writer put it: "When perestroika started and all the heroes of the previous years had been shattered to dust, the only remaining, real, tangible hero was Gagarin; the first man in space, and a good guy whom both the elderly and the young trusted."

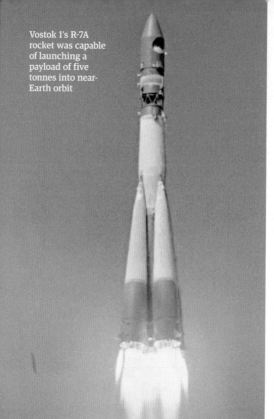
Vostok 1's R-7A rocket was capable of launching a payload of five tonnes into near-Earth orbit

Hailed as a hero both during and after communism, Gagarin's legacy is a unique unifying force

Of the 250 candidates brought in for testing, Yuri Gagarin was among the space programme's 'Vanguard Six'

"After sifting through 3,000 pilots' records, the team initially brought in 250 prospective candidates"

orbit, the pressure was on - failure at this critical juncture would completely undermine the Soviets' cumulative propaganda victories. With the Americans planning to fly the first manned suborbital Mercury mission in 1961, a Soviet document - On a Plan for the Mastery of Cosmic Space - required all testing to be completed by the end of the year.

By now the project had a name: Vostok, or 'East'. Comprising of three vessels - 1K, 2K and 3KA - the first was a reconnaissance satellite, and the third the actual piloted spacecraft. The policy governing the programme required all assemblies, instruments and systems to be tested and certified 'Suitable for 3KA'. The military carried out thorough checks, with chief designers and section heads personally liable for their components, ushering in a new age of quality and consistency for the Soviet space programme.

One early Vostok mission, Korabl-Sputnik 2, carried an assortment of lifeforms into orbit, notably the dogs Belka and Strekla, becoming the first to bring animals back to Earth safely. However, Korolev was concerned that Belka had clearly become distressed during the fourth orbit, and had vomited due to weightlessness. As a result he decided to restrict his manned mission to no more than one orbit, with the ship controlled automatically from the ground and a manual override code handed to the pilot in a sealed envelope - just in case.

Returning to Earth, the braking rocket engine would need to fire its thrust in the opposite direction from the craft's orbital velocity vector. Once the braking burn had been applied the spacecraft would execute a braking turn - the atmosphere slamming the brakes on the remaining energy. The craft would communicate with Earth via a variety of radio links, along with the capacity to broadcast TV from space.

As the project grew increasingly complex, so too did the bureaucracy of OKB-1, as the Council of Chief Designers watched their power dissipate among designers and organisations representing different disciplines. Though the Council of Six remained, Korolev had to bring in 15 new voting members, representing a variety of bodies from the Institute of Aviation Medicine to Air Force Command. Korolev succeeded in establishing himself atop this new hierarchy - named the rocket-space complex - delegating to his deputies, who in turn worked with their relevant chief designers. While the old guard did their best to mitigate risk, young engineers threw caution to the wind, creating a healthy balance of ambition and control.

In 1960, only two of five Korabl-Sputnik launches went into orbit and made it back. With a 'soft landing' system still years away, the only way of ensuring a safe landing for the astronaut was a two-step landing system, which ejected the cosmonaut out of the descent module with a parachute. The following year two further missions carried animals and mannequins into space, safely ejecting the dummy, 'Ivan Ivanovich'.

After sifting through 3,000 pilots' records, the team initially brought in 250 prospective candidates. This number was slowly whittled away by medical examinations, vigorous rotating chair training for weightlessness and ten-day isolation chambers. Of the 12 candidates selected by the Air Force to enter the Cosmonauts Training Center, the six most promising were dubbed the 'Vanguard Six'. Among the six was a young man called Yuri Gagarin, who persevered through the intense training and the Vostok simulator, TDK-1, the first of its kind in the USSR.

Though the Vostok spacecraft was controlled from the ground, a team member secretly informed Gagarin of the override code in advance

The Vostok programme ushered in a new era of efficiency, centred around the Baikonur Cosmodrome

Finally, in March 1961, Korolev recommended the launch of a Vostok spacecraft with a human aboard, approved the next month. Gagarin was selected to pilot the vehicle, with Gherman Titov his backup.

12 April was an auspicious day, marked by a clear, sunny sky over the top-secret launch site in Baikonur, Kazakhstan. Gagarin hugged his comrades and stepped onto the elevator before entering the descent module. When technicians discovered the hatch was not sealed properly, they had to spend an hour resealing it, during which time Gagarin asked for music to be played over the radio.

Leaning back into his foam-padded ejection seat, he yelled, "Off we go," and away Vostok went. Two minutes later the four strap-on boosters ran out of propellant and fell away, and minutes later the rocket core stage followed suit. As the craft soared into space, Gagarin beamed through the radio: "Visibility is excellent! Out the window I see Earth, clouds, I see rivers. It's beautiful."

His spherical cabin featured three portholes, a life-support system, radios and various instrumentation. An attached service module housed batteries, orientation rockets, a retro system and other equipment. Having completed a single orbit and travelling 27,359 kilometres (17,000 miles) per hour, the service module detached and the descent module returned to Earth, with Gagarin ejecting safely. Despite some hiccups along the way, such as a brief detachment scare, the Soviets had done it.

After landing, Gagarin, clad in an orange suit with a white helmet, encountered a farmer and his daughter. "When they saw me in my spacesuit, and the parachute dragging alongside as I walked, they started to back away in fear. I told them, 'Don't be afraid. I am a Soviet like you, who has descended from space, and I must find a telephone to call Moscow!'"

The psychological impact on both the US and USSR was profound - the Soviets emerged the masters of space and technology, and with the US 25 days away from suborbital flight, they would have to set themselves a profoundly ambitious task to return from a defeat of this magnitude.

Reactions to Vostok

The Vostok success elicited powerful reactions of joy and fear across the world

The Vostok mission captured the imagination of the world, a potent symbol of socialism's success

Thousands paraded across Moscow, chanting 'cosmonaut' to rousing music blasted from loudspeakers. The celebrations continued across the country, as Khrushchev gloated to Gagarin: "Let the capitalist countries try to catch up with our country, which has blazed a trail into space and which has launched the world's first cosmonaut."

Indian Prime Minister Jawaharlal Nehru congratulated the USSR on "a great human victory of man over the forces of nature". Indonesia, meanwhile, said it marked "an entirely new era in human life", hoping it would "have only a beneficial influence on mankind".

Yomiuri newspaper in Tokyo noted that "real competition" was "just beginning", but encouraged the US and USSR to "use their new knowledge and techniques for the good of mankind".

Despite the humiliating blow, President Kennedy extended the Soviet scientists and engineers a cordial congratulations: "It is my sincere desire that in the continuing quest for knowledge of outer space, our nations can work together to obtain the greatest benefit to mankind."

While Wernher von Braun celebrated the "remarkable" achievement, the 'father' of the hydrogen bomb, Edward Teller, said the US' failure to put a man in space first was the result of "years of unimaginative, materialistic thinking".

The German daily, *Die Welt*, said the USSR was now reaping "the benefits of its purposeful efforts", adding: "It could have been avoided. For weeks the Americans had at their disposal the technical know-how required to send a man into space and get him back."

Meanwhile, the director of the School of Physical Sciences at the Australian National University dismissed the mission as "just a stunt", compared to previous accomplishments.

Vostok's success was a source of pride for Soviet citizens, who considered it a victory of socialism over capitalism

Vostok 1 featured a detachable, spherical descent module, from which Gagarin ejected with a parachute

In the lead-up to Vostok, the Korabl-Sputnik 4 and 5 missions successfully carried the dogs Chernushka and Zvezdochka into orbit, and brought them home safely

Khrushchev celebrates alongside Gagarin, right, and Gherman Titov, the backup pilot for Vostok 1, who went on to become the second man in orbit

MYSTERIES OF THE UNIVERSE

YURI GAGARIN

WAS HE REALLY THE FIRST MAN IN SPACE?

Before the cosmonaut orbited the Earth, rumours abounded that someone else already had

Reported by David Crookes

Everybody knows that Neil Armstrong was the first person to set foot on the Moon. Most people are also aware that he wasn't the first to go into space. After all, Alan Shepard paved the way for American astronauts on 5 May 1961, while Soviet cosmonaut Yuri Gagarin stole a march by rocketing into space a few weeks earlier on 12 April.

Or did he?

Today Gagarin's name is cemented in the record books, and he instantly became a national hero across the Soviet Union. Presented as a triumph of the fiercely fought Space Race against the US, the 27 year old, who had been chosen just three days before the mission, spent 108 minutes in space, orbited the Earth and returned fit and well following a drama-filled flight.

And yet, before he even embarked on his journey skywards, doubt was seeded in many a person's mind. For rumours had surfaced that the Soviets had successfully launched a man into space before Gagarin set foot in Vostok 1, and the talk was that

Yuri's flight path

Gagarin was calm prior to his ascent into space, despite being the first human to do so

Eye on the world
A large window in the capsule ensured Gagarin was able to see the outer surroundings of space. It was covered by a payload shroud during the launch.

4. Revolving around the Earth
Gagarin was able to make a single revolution of Earth on a journey of 40,868.6 kilometres (25,394.8 miles), which took 108 minutes.

3. Reaching orbit
On its ascent and as it reached orbit, the final rocket stage shut down and dropped from the spacecraft. The capsule reached a maximum height of 327 kilometres (203 miles).

2. Separation
At 06:09 four strap-on boosters broke away from the rocket, having depleted their propellant. Three minutes later the rocket's core stage separated from the spacecraft and final rocket stage.

5. Ejecting
The descent capsule separated when the spacecraft was seven kilometres (4.3-miles) above the ground at 07:55, its hatch releas and Gagarin was ejected.

The instrument module
The conical component of Vostok 1 contained the engine system and the oxygen and nitrogen tanks. This separated away during the descent.

Gagarin's module
The Vostok 1 spacecraft had a spherical descent module fitted with a heat shield. It contained the instruments and an escape system, including an ejector seat.

1. Blast off
Yuri Gagarin's Vostok 1 spacecraft launched on 12 April 1961 at 06:07 UTC blasting off from the Baikonur Cosmodrome, a spaceport in southern Kazakhstan.

6. Landing safely on Earth
Parachutes brought both Gagarin and the capsule back to Earth. It took ten minutes for Gagarin to land in a field in the Saratov region of Russia. He made a call to Moscow.

© Adrian Mann pedrosala

one cosmonaut had done so on 7 April, just five days earlier.

Dennis Ogden, the Moscow-based correspondent for the British Communist Party newspaper, *Daily Worker*, reported as such, his story splashed across the publication's front page with the headline: 'The First Man In Space'. It informed readers that the spaceman – "the test-pilot son of a top-ranking aircraft designer" – was "back alive, but suffering from [the] effects of his flight". Gagarin's feet hadn't even left the ground when the paper hit the newsstands, and it caused something of a stir. The first whispers of a conspiracy theory which has continued to this day. The Soviet Union denied the reports and instead alerted the press to Gagarin's subsequent feat. Ogden also reported this, his article again making the splash as he wrote of a "hero's welcome" and a Soviet Union "wild with joy at [the] first trip outside this world".

Ogden's article could have been seen as something akin to a correction; confirmation that he was initially wrong about the flight on 7 April. But then French journalist Eduard Bobrovsky followed up on Ogden's claims and pointed to the man in question as being an accomplished test pilot called Vladimir Ilyushin, while also stating the flight actually took place on 25 March. Trouble is, his mission had – according to the press sources – not gone quite as well as planned. That is why, it has long since been claimed, Ilyushin's feat was cast aside in favour of Gagarin's successful launch and landing.

Ilyushin was a Soviet general and a test pilot of high standing. He had broken many a speed and altitude record and his father was influential, having designed and built Second World War fighters and

"Rumours surfaced that the Soviets had successfully launched a man into space before Gagarin"

bombers. Ilyushin senior had also earned himself a place in government. To that end, his son would have been seen as the perfect person to send into space, his penchant for risk taking such that the then-34-year-old pilot would have surely relished the task. And so the story went that his journey outwards on board his spaceship was fine but, after three supposed orbits, Ilyushin's return went awry. Apparently his landing was off-course, causing him physical harm and mental anguish. There was even a suggestion that the accident had put him into a coma.

"The space vessel reportedly was recovered where expected, but Ilyushin was mentally unbalanced and is unconscious in a Moscow hospital," said a report in *The Spokesman Review* about the journalist's claims on 22 April 1961. The article added that Bobrovsky said his information came from reliable sources that he could not name and that Russian officers denied the report. Indeed, the Soviet Union claimed Ilyushin was in hospital being treated for injuries he had received in a car accident.

The Soviets were not the only ones blinking with disbelief at this. Even the Americans did not believe the journalists' claims. Indeed, Pierre Salinger, the press secretary to the White House at the time, told

Below: The Vostok-K (8K72K) rocket carried Gagarin and the Vostok 1 spacecraft to orbital altitude

The lost cosmonauts?

Aleksei Ledovsky
1957
A top-ranking communist from Czechoslovakia claimed Ledovsky had died, having been launched in a converted R-5A rocket on a suborbital flight from Kapustin Yar rocket base. There is no evidence of a manned Soviet suborbital spaceflight.

Andrei Mikov
1959
Another said to have died on a suborbital flight, as reported by the Italian news agency Continentale. This was stated as having happened a year after cosmonaut Serenti Shiborin was killed in the same way.

Two, unknown
1961
The Italian Judica-Cordiglia brothers claimed to have picked up the sound of a dying, unconscious man, as well as a failing human heartbeat, with the suggestion that these were from two Soviets who had suffered a failed re-entry.

Unknown
1961
It is suggested that a manned Vostok orbital launch took place on 16 May 1961 and that, following 17 orbits around Earth, depletion of the spacecraft's oxygen supplies caused the cosmonaut to suffocate.

Pyotr Dolgov
1962
The story is that Dolgov died during a parachute jump at high altitude from a Volga balloon gondola on 1 November 1962 after hitting a part of the gondola, depressurising his suit. There have been reports he actually perished in a failed Vostok flight.

The theories

Vladimir Ilyushin circled Earth three times

Dennis Ogden suggested a cosmonaut had successfully completed a manned spaceflight on 7 April 1961 but it had left him incapacitated, forcing Russia to find someone else to face the public.

Vladimir Ilyushin crashed in China

Further embellishments claimed Ilyushin had crashed in China and was not only injured but in the hands of the Chinese, who refused to release him.

Vladimir Ilyushin was an obvious choice

One of the reasons why Ilyushin's name crops up in relation to this conspiracy theory is that his background was conducive to a space mission. He was an accomplished test pilot.

Yuri Gagarin was the first person in space

Ilyushin is thought to have been involved in a car accident and he is not understood to have been in the cosmonaut group. For that reason, he never did go into space.

Below: The general consensus is that Yuri Gagarin was the first to orbit the Earth

Below right: The Vostok 1 capsule used by Yuri Gagarin, which is on display outside of Moscow at the RKK Energiya museum

reporters that there was no evidence of a flight on 7 April and, we have to assume, nothing to have raised suspicion in March either. NORAD space tracking stations, it transpired, had not picked up on anything, and the US was not about to leap in and heap embarrassment on the Soviet Union without proof.

And yet, even this wasn't enough to completely quell suspicion. Some journalists reckoned the claims of a car crash were a mere cover story, and it certainly wasn't beyond the wildest of imaginations to believe the Soviets would seek to bury a mistake, since it had been done so many times in the past. What's more, in the framework of the Space Race, conspiracists could surmise there was a valid reason for trying to bury such a failure: the Soviets would constantly pull out all the stops to present communism as the superior ideology.

But is that, together with unknown journalistic sources, reason enough to believe that Gagarin's place in history was not quite what it was? Ogden would later claim that he saw a photograph of Ilyushin wearing space gear at the time of the supposed flight, but it has never subsequently surfaced. Meanwhile, Ilyushin himself – who died in 2010, aged 82 – never confessed to having flown into space. He lived to tell the claimed tale, but notably did not.

What we have seen, however, are rumours continuing to swirl long after the event, and they've even been fleshed out. One of the most notable was a 52-minute documentary in 1999 called *The Cosmonaut Cover-Up*, released by Global Science

Productions and directed by Dr Elliott Haimoff who, in the following year, also helmed *Vladimir Ilyushin: The Real First Man in Space*.

Widely broadcast, it claimed Ilyushin had failed to eject from his capsule, crashed into China and, after being captured, was eventually handed back to the USSR in 1962. The documentary makers said Ilyushin wouldn't talk about the alleged incidents on camera and preferred to maintain his secrecy. But was Ilyushin so fearful that, in verifying such claims, he would open himself up to a world in which he did not wish to boldly go? Given that the documentary was being made a number of years after the collapse of the Soviet Union, when secrets were finally being divulged and historical events were being flung open, you would suspect not.

In fact, the Soviets began to open up well before the USSR ceased to be. In 1980 the West finally learned of the death of Valentin Bondarenko, who died ten days into a 15-day low-pressure endurance experiment in Moscow in 1961 when fire broke out, even though they had removed his image from an official subsequent training photograph. It took longer to tell the world of a major launchpad accident which took place on 24 October 1960 and officially killed 78, as eventually revealed to the rest of the world in 1989. There's talk of Gagarin being used for propaganda, but of all the confessions and documents seen since the Soviet Union collapsed, Ilyushin has never featured.

And yet there have been some peculiar pieces of 'evidence'. Two Italian former

> "Ilyushin himself – who died in 2010, aged 82 – never confessed to having flown into space"

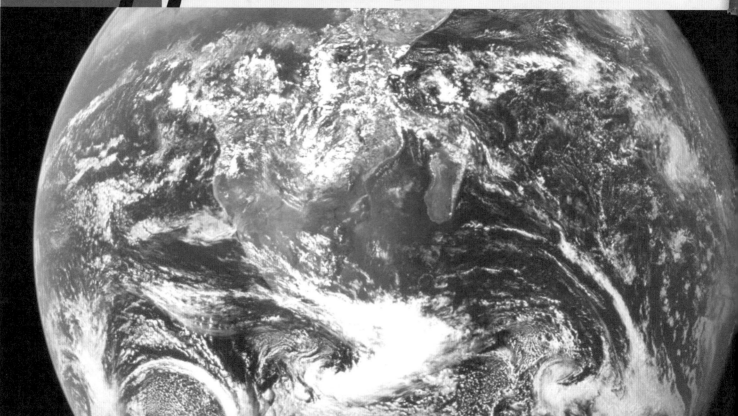

Yuri Gagarin's scrapbook

Getting ready for space requires great dedication, as shown in these photos of the first man to go

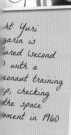

Left: Wearing his overalls and oxygen mask, the effects of space are tested on Yuri Gagarin's body in 1958

Right: Taking some time out to relax during his training, this image was taken following his journey back to Earth

Left: Yuri Gagarin is pictured (second ?) with a cosmonaut training group, checking the space equipment in 1960

Left: Yuri Gagarin assumes his lying down position, as he would inside the space capsule

Right: Yuri Gagarin trains in the Vostok spacecraft in November 1960, five months before his history-making flight

amateur radio operators, Achille and Giovanni Judica-Cordiglia, claimed to have recorded audio from an orbiting capsule in the days before Gagarin made his flight, and it was actually the fourth slice of startling audio released by the pair. The first was from May 1960 of a manned spacecraft reportedly going off-course; the second in November that year of an SOS Morse code from a trouble spacecraft leaving Earth's orbit and, most chillingly, a third in 1961 of a cosmonaut apparently suffocating to death. Should these be hard-and-fast evidence of spaceflights, then we would have to say that not only was Gagarin not the first person into space, Ilyushin was perhaps not first either. But given the supposition was that everyone involved in those three recordings had died, discovering the truth has been even more difficult. And yet theories still mount up.

Indeed, what could we make of claims by Mikhail Rudenko, a former Soviet senior engineer and experimenter with Experimental Design Office

456, who in 2001 told the Russian internet news website **pravda.ru**, formed in 1999 by members of the editorial staff of the oldest Soviet paper *Pravda*, that cosmonauts had been sent into space in 1957, 1958 and 1959.

"All three pilots died during the flights and their names were never officially published," he is quoted as saying, having explained that the pilots involved were called Ledovskikh, Shaborin and Mitkov and took part in sub-orbital flights. "The cosmonauts were to reach space heights in the highest point of such an orbit and then return to the Earth," he added. But considering *Pravda* has also run with headlines such as 'Aliens forced Americans out from the Moon' and 'Alien and human skulls found on Mars', it's a tough call!

Harder still to determine is Ilyushin's location in March and April 1961. The Soviets didn't help themselves in this regard either because they couldn't give a straight answer about the reason why he was seen to be injured - pinned down

Sequence of events

What's thought to have happened
What actually happened

★ **Vladimir Ilyushin becomes a Soviet test pilot**
Born to the Soviet aircraft designer Sergei Vladimirovich Ilyushin, Vladimir Ilyushin fulfilled his dream of wanting to become a test pilot of the best Russian aircraft.

★ **He is made a Hero of the Soviet Union**
Having built a reputation as a pilot, Ilyushin broke records, bringing him to the attention of the Soviet space programme.

★ **Ilyushin heads into space**
Newspaper reports suggested he had flown into space in secret on 7 April 1961. It was later claimed a spacecraft failure saw him land in China. ●

★ **Yuri Gagarin named as the first man in space**
On 12 April 1961, Yuri Gagarin completed his flight and the Soviets named him – not Ilyushin – as the first man to journey into space.

1950 1952 1955 1960 1961 1961 1962 1968 1970

★ **Yuri Gagarin enters flight training**
Yuri Gagarin enrols at the Orenburg Pilot School and gains his pilot wings in a MiG-15. He became a senior lieutenant in November 1959.

★ **Chosen as a prospective cosmonaut**
Having excelled, Yuri Gagarin is picked with 19 other pilots during a secret selection process to find cosmonauts. He is chosen for elite training. ●

★ **Picked to fly into space**
His progress was so good that he and Gherman Titov were selected for the first launch. It also helped that he could fit in the Vostok capsule.

"Supposing Russia had suffered such terrible space attempts, would it really have announced Gagarin's flight?"

Right: The 1981 ruble coin issued to commemorate the 20th anniversary of Gagarin's space flight

to that car crash - or when it actually took place. Neither could they offer up a suitable explanation for why he might have been in China. They also went as far as to say he was never actually a cosmonaut and, indeed, it would appear that he wasn't in the original cosmonaut team. No memoirs or declassified information put him there.

Yet it's also difficult to corroborate the Judica-Cordiglia recordings with any data from official sources. Listening stations did not pick up on what they claimed to have committed to tape, and radio astronomer Bernard Lovell, who established the Jodrell Bank Observatory in Cheshire, England, dismissed claims of earlier Russian manned space attempts in 1963. Even that, however, isn't as clear cut as it sounds.

Lovell paid visits to Russia around this time, and there have even been allegations that he was brainwashed. He fell ill that year following such a trip, and the UK Ministry of Defence said it might have

been due to an attempt to remove his memory of a Soviet offer to build a telescope facility in the USSR. His son says he was merely ill from exhaustion, and that sounds more plausible.

Besides, supposing Russia had suffered such terrible space attempts which resulted in deaths and crashes, would it really have announced Gagarin's flight in the way it did? As James E. Oberg points out in a 1975 article he wrote in *Space World* magazine, the Russian news agency TASS – frequently used as a front organisation by the Soviet intelligence agency - released its first bulletin while Gagarin was still in-flight. If it was worried about the potential for bad news, wouldn't it have been better to wait until the mission was over and Gagarin's feet were firmly back on the ground, rather than risk Gagarin's spacecraft hitting the same problems as the one claimed to have taken place just days before?

Maybe we will never know. As we've mentioned, the two men who would have been directly involved are not around any more - Gagarin was killed when the MiG-15 training jet he was piloting crashed on 27 March 1968 when he was 34. Given the evidence that has been made available, the smart money remains on Gagarin having been the first person on a manned spaceflight. Sure, Russian space history can be murky and difficult to pick

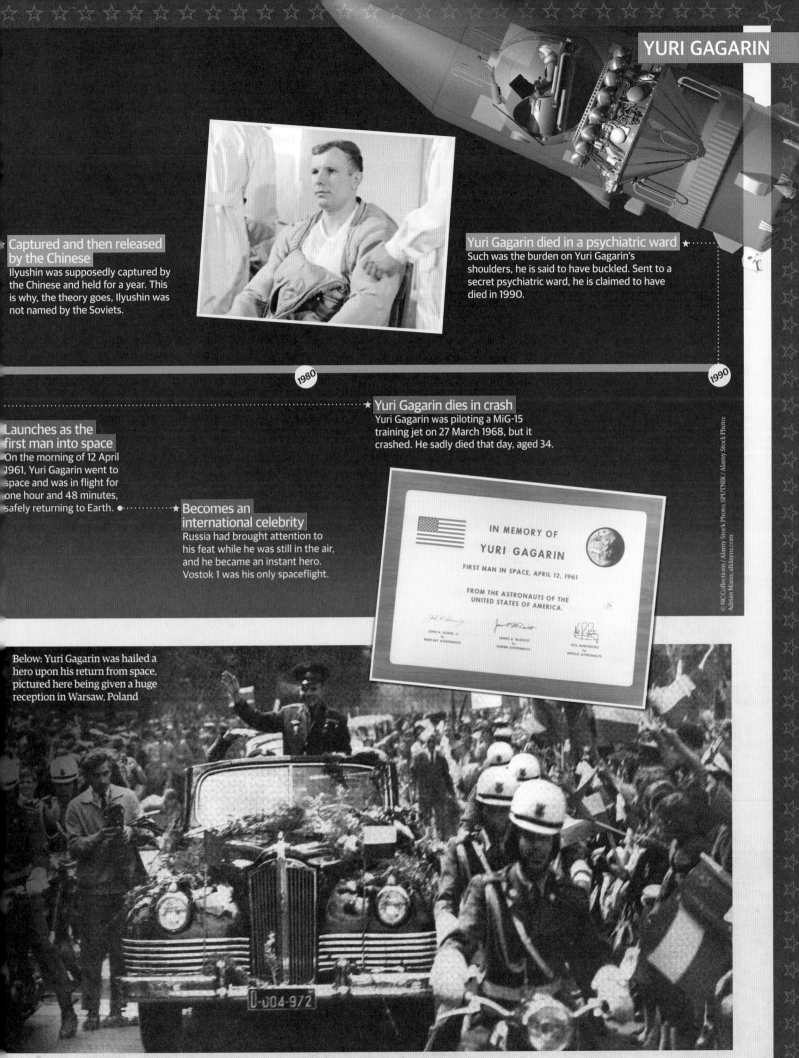

★ **Captured and then released by the Chinese**
Ilyushin was supposedly captured by the Chinese and held for a year. This is why, the theory goes, Ilyushin was not named by the Soviets.

Yuri Gagarin died in a psychiatric ward ★
Such was the burden on Yuri Gagarin's shoulders, he is said to have buckled. Sent to a secret psychiatric ward, he is claimed to have died in 1990.

1980

1990

★ **Yuri Gagarin dies in crash**
Yuri Gagarin was piloting a MiG-15 training jet on 27 March 1968, but it crashed. He sadly died that day, aged 34.

Launches as the first man into space
On the morning of 12 April 1961, Yuri Gagarin went to space and was in flight for one hour and 48 minutes, safely returning to Earth. ●

★ **Becomes an international celebrity**
Russia had brought attention to his feat while he was still in the air, and he became an instant hero. Vostok 1 was his only spaceflight.

IN MEMORY OF

YURI GAGARIN

FIRST MAN IN SPACE, APRIL 12, 1961

FROM THE ASTRONAUTS OF THE
UNITED STATES OF AMERICA.

JOHN H. GLENN, JR.
for
MERCURY ASTRONAUTS

JAMES A. McDIVITT
for
GEMINI ASTRONAUTS

NEIL ARMSTRONG
for
APOLLO ASTRONAUTS

Below: Yuri Gagarin was hailed a hero upon his return from space, pictured here being given a huge reception in Warsaw, Poland

Learning to fly

Project Gemini formed a bridge between NASA's first Mercury flights and the Apollo Moon programme

The historic flight of Soviet cosmonaut Yuri Gagarin on 12 April 1961 plunged the United States into a crisis of confidence - if their Cold War rival was so far ahead in space, what else might they be capable of? The Mercury programme would be America's immediate response, but President John F Kennedy realised that a long-term solution was needed, refocusing US space policy on an ambitious target that would, over several years, allow NASA to fight its way back into the Space Race. Six weeks later, Kennedy announced a new goal in space to Congress - America was going to the Moon.

NASA officials knew that getting there would call for an array of new techniques and technology. Aside from powerful new rockets, potential schemes for putting people on the Moon all required rendezvous and docking of spacecraft and components in orbit - flight manoeuvres far beyond the Mercury capsule's basic capabilities.

With the Apollo spacecraft still on the drawing board, there was a clear need for an intermediate vehicle - something capable of supporting more than one astronaut on longer missions, manoeuvring in orbit and testing various technical procedures that might be needed en route to the Moon. This new spacecraft was to be known as Project Gemini.

Once the basic requirements had been established, the Gemini spacecraft was developed and built at breakneck speed. Although superficially similar in appearance to a scaled-up Mercury capsule, it was far more capable. A pressurised 're-entry module' seated two astronauts side-by-side in a cockpit environment that was designed in consultation with the Mercury astronauts (particularly Gus Grissom) and appealed to their test-pilot mindset.

Beneath this in a conical stack sat two more elements - the 'retrograde module' whose rockets would be used to return from orbit, and the 'equipment module' carrying batteries, propellant, water and other supplies. An important advance came with the introduction of fuel-cell technology that could generate electricity using liquid oxygen and hydrogen, reducing the need for heavy batteries and permitting longer-duration flights. Thruster nozzles dotted across the surface of all three elements allowed a Gemini craft to change its orbit and orientation in space.

The first Gemini spacecraft was launched on 8 April 1964 using a Titan II rocket. This derivative of the US Air Force's Titan ballistic missile, a fairly simple and reliable rocket whose fuels ignited on contact (avoiding the need for a complex ignition system), was used for launches throughout the Gemini programme.

Fitted with test equipment in place of a crew, the Gemini 1 spacecraft appeared to perform well in orbit, but was not designed for recovery. A second test, in January 1965, assessed the splashdown procedure and allowed NASA engineers to see how the spacecraft had coped with re-entry to the Earth's atmosphere.

With no significant problems encountered, NASA gave the go-ahead for a manned launch. Gemini 3 launched on 23 March 1965, pairing Grissom with a new astronaut, John W Young. The shakedown flight lasted a mere three orbits, but the spacecraft systems worked perfectly and the only significant incident occurred when Young produced a corned-beef sandwich he had smuggled aboard, sharing a few bites with Grissom. Despite being reprimanded by his superiors afterwards, Young would go on to have an illustrious NASA career, flying in both the Apollo and Space Shuttle programmes.

The path was now clear for a more ambitious mission in the form of Gemini 4. Crewed by two

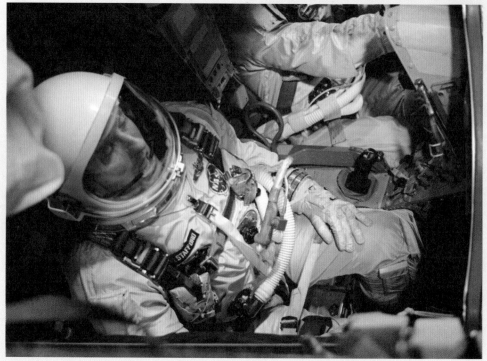

new astronauts, James McDivitt and Ed White, this June flight lasted a little over four days. During the mission, the astronauts successfully carried out a range of on-board experiments, although attempts to change orbit and rendezvous with the spacecraft's own Titan II upper stage ended in failure.

However, such problems were outshone by an iconic success, as White opened his hatch and became the first US astronaut to walk in space. White remained tethered to the spacecraft throughout his 'Extra-Vehicular Activity' (EVA), but he was able to float free and manoeuvre using a 'zip gun' that fired a jet of gas in one direction to push him in the other. Although the Soviets had achieved their first spacewalk a few months before, White's longer EVA went far more smoothly, and delivered stunning photographs of an astronaut floating in space – at last, it seemed, NASA was catching up in the Space Race.

Gemini 7 as seen from Gemini 6 during the first US rendezvous in space

"Gemini 5 spent eight days in orbit, smashing the five-day space endurance record previously held by the Soviets"

That message was reinforced when Gemini 5, launched in August 1965, spent eight days in orbit, smashing the five-day space endurance record previously held by the Soviet Vostok 5. The mission paired Mercury veteran L Gordon Cooper with newcomer Charles "Pete" Conrad Jr, and was the first to match the duration of the planned lunar flights. Not everything went smoothly, however – issues with the fuel cells meant electricity had to be rationed – a planned rendezvous with an unmanned 'pod' was scaled back to a more basic manoeuvring test, and other experiments had to be abandoned (leading Conrad to remark at one point that he wished he'd brought a book with him to pass the time).

Although many aspects of Gemini had now proved successful, pressure was mounting for the next mission to pull off the long-awaited orbital rendezvous. Gemini 6, planned for launch on 25 October, was intended to rendezvous with a special unmanned 'Agena target vehicle' (ATV) that would launch shortly ahead of it. Mercury astronaut Wally Schirra and his colleague Thomas Stafford were sitting aboard their spacecraft ready for launch when news came through that the ATV had been lost after an explosion.

With Gemini 7 already planned for a December launch on a 14-day endurance mission, it seemed that Gemini 6 had lost its launch window, and the opportunity for a successful rendezvous would have to wait until the following year. But then

Frank Borman and Jim Lovell, the Gemini 7 crew, made a daring suggestion: why not use their own spacecraft as Gemini 6's rendezvous target? After some convincing, NASA officials signed off on the idea – Gemini 6 (redesignated Gemini 6-A) launched on 15 December, towards the end of Borman and Lovell's mission. And this time, everything went smoothly, with Schirra and Stafford steering their capsule to within 30 cm (12 in) of Gemini 7.

1966 saw ever-more daring missions for Gemini, as NASA geared up for the planned first flights of the Apollo spacecraft the following year. Gemini 8, launched in March, was crewed by two newcomers who would both go on to command Apollo lunar missions – Neil Armstrong and David Scott. They docked successfully with an ATV at last (the first ever docking in orbit), but shortly afterwards a jammed thruster set the linked spacecraft into a dangerous spin that forced them to cut the mission short for safety reasons.

Gemini 9-A (the designation indicated the use of its reserve crew, Thomas Stafford and Gene Cernan,

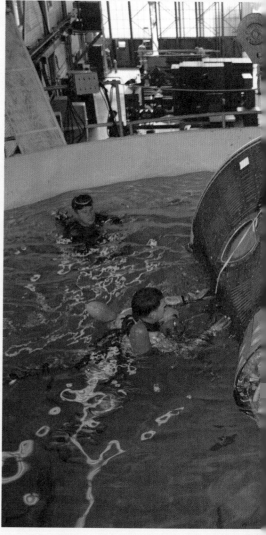

after the primary crew died in an air crash) also hit a number of problems. When the spacecraft approached its ATV docking target in June, it found that the protective shroud around it had failed to come away, making docking impossible. Cernan also had trouble accessing an 'astronaut manoeuvring unit' jetpack that he was supposed to wear during a spacewalk.

Fortunately, this was the programme's last major setback. Gemini 10, launched the following month with John Young and Michael Collins aboard, not only docked with its own ATV, but then steered to a rendezvous with the Gemini 8 target vehicle, allowing Collins to inspect the abandoned spacecraft during an EVA. Gemini 11 saw Pete Conrad and Richard Gordon set a new altitude record of 1,374 km (854 miles), and even generated artificial gravity by tethering the spacecraft and its ATV, then setting them in a slow spin around each other.

The twelfth and final Gemini mission was brief but equally ambitious. Crewed by Buzz Aldrin and Jim Lovell, it spent four days in orbit rehearsing many of the docking and rendezvous techniques that would be required by the Apollo missions. In addition, Aldrin carried out a complex two-hour spacewalk using new handgrips to clamber around the capsule and practice servicing it in space. By the time Gemini 12 splashed down on 15 November 1966, the stage was set for the debut of Apollo.

The Gemini 6 prime crew, pictured during water egress training at Ellington Air Force Base, Texas, in 1965

Docking in space

Gemini's docking system consisted of a probe mounted on the end of the manned spacecraft that locked into a conical receptor on the end of the target vehicle. Gemini 11 pilot Richard Gordon compared it to the mid-air refuelling mechanism on a jet fighter. Once securely docked, controls in the Gemini capsule allowed the astronauts to control the engine and thrusters on the target vehicle.

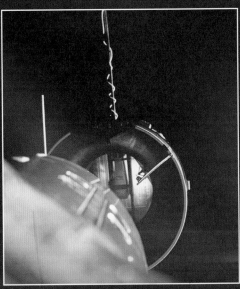

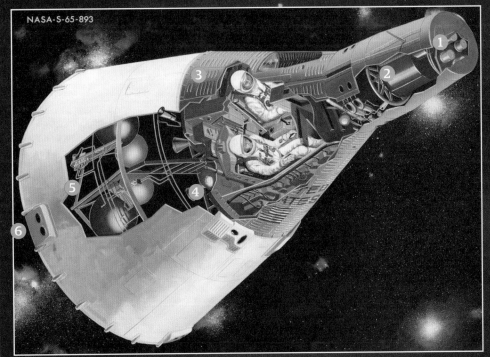

NASA-S-65-893

1 Rendezvous antenna
This antenna extended from the spacecraft during docking operations and slid into a cone on the target vehicle.

2 Parachute system
During re-entry, Gemini employed a small drogue before its main parachutes – early plans to use a paraglider system were abandoned.

3 Crew hatches
Twin hatches allowed access for the astronauts – EVAs were carried out simply by the astronaut opening the hatch and standing up in his seat.

4 Retrograde module
Situated behind the re-entry module, the retro module housed four solid rockets. During re-entry, the spacecraft reversed its orientation to point backwards along its orbit, and fired these rockets to slow down.

5 Equipment module
The rearmost Gemini module contained equipment to power and sustain the spacecraft on missions that were going to be up to two weeks long, including batteries and fuel cells, water and oxygen.

6 Attitude control thrusters
Thrusters positioned at various points around the Gemini spacecraft could be fired in sequence to change the vehicle's orientation and manoeuvre in space.

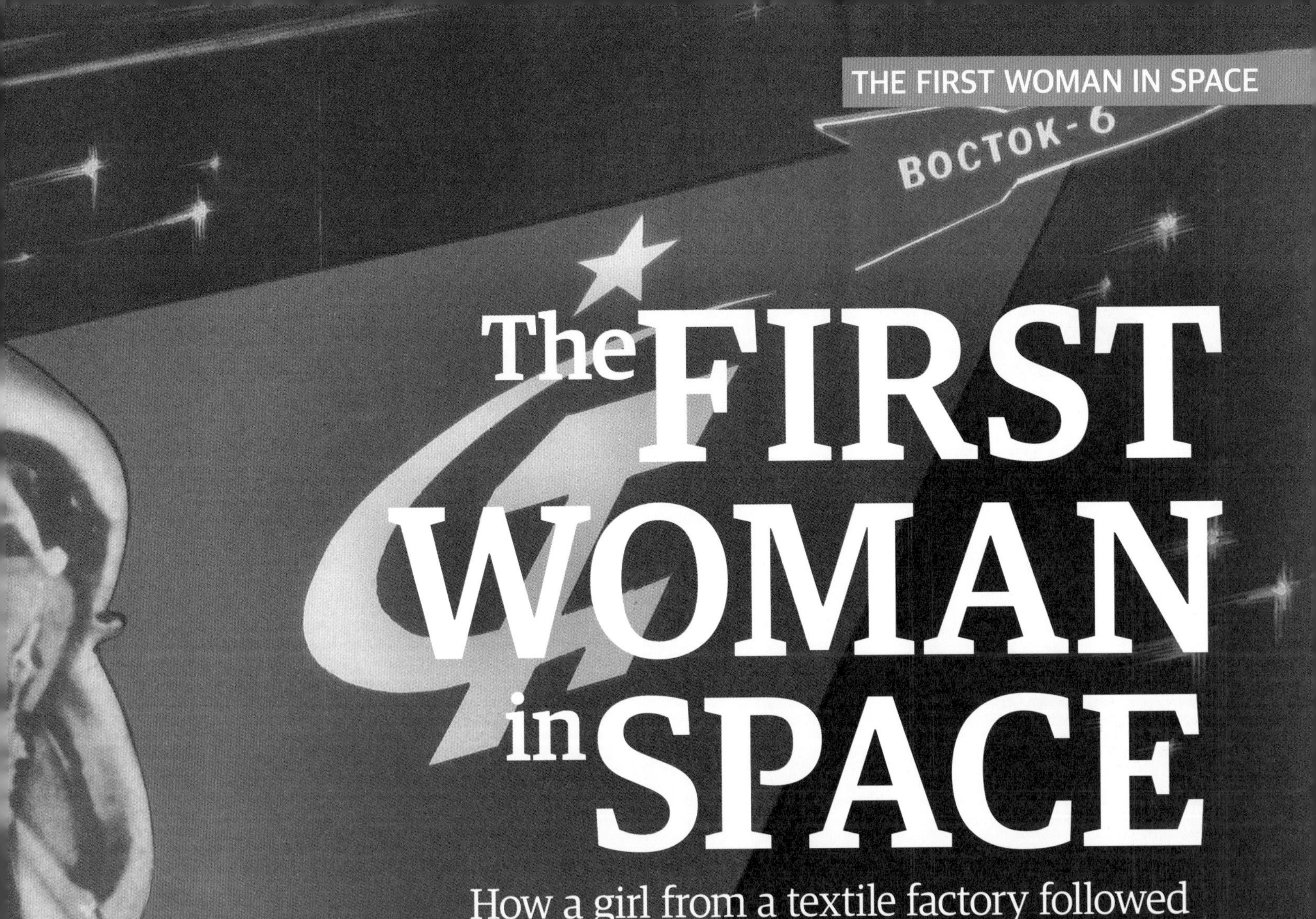

ВОСТОК - 6

The FIRST WOMAN in SPACE

How a girl from a textile factory followed her dreams and reached the stars

Written by Frances White

The humble beginnings of Valentina Tereshkova could never have predicted the ripples she was fated to create across the globe. She was born on 6 March 1937 in the village of Maslennikovo, approximately 270 kilometres (170 miles) from Moscow. Her parents were migrants from Belarus, with her mother working in a textile plant and her father a tractor driver. Sadly, her father was killed during World War II. Tereshkova's education in her youth was minimal; she didn't attend school until she was eight years old, and she left when she turned 16, joining her mother in the textile factory. However, despite having to leave school to make a living, she continued to pursue education through correspondence courses from an industrial school.

Although her life seemed destined to be spent in the same textile factory as her mother, and confined to the same small village, Tereshkova had unusual hobbies and interests, ones that would open up a world of possibilities. One of these was parachuting. She had been interested in parachuting from a young age, and joined the Yaroslavi Air Sports Club. She made her first jump aged just 22. Not just a thrill seeker, she was also

> "Tereshkova had been interested in parachuting from a young age"

an intellectual, fascinated by politics. She joined the local Young Communist League and became secretary in 1961, and later joined the Communist Party of the Soviet Union. Tereshkova was not happy with a life confined to a textile mill... she wanted more. She wanted to fling herself from planes, and then afterwards debate the nation's issues. Though some critics would later claim she was no more than a puppet for the country to tug the strings of, it's clear to see that from an early age Tereshkova was driven to shoot for the stars.

It was the flight of Yuri Gagarin in 1961, the first human to travel into outer space, that would truly transform Tereshkova's life. After having already put the first man into space, Sergei Korolev, the chief Soviet rocket engineer, decided that it was time to do the same again, but this time with a woman. Tereshkova was immediately interested, and volunteered for the Soviet space programme.

There were over 400 applicants, and Tereshkova was selected along with four others. Tereshkova benefited hugely from her parachuting experience. At the time she had completed 126 jumps, and cosmonauts were required to parachute from their capsules before they hit the ground upon returning

Tereshkova was not only the first woman to fly in space, but also the first civilian

Vostok 6 was the last flight of a Vostok SKA spacecraft

Vostok 6
How the craft and suit were designed to carry Tereshkova into history

Although spaceflight sounds glamorous now, the conditions that Tereshkova had to endure were anything but. Far from the roomier spacecraft we see today, the Vostok 6 consisted of a spherical cabin covered with ablative material. She was strapped to an ejection seat inside the pressurised cabin, which was only 2.3-metres (7.5-feet) wide. Tereshkova was able to glimpse the Earth through three small portholes. The cabin contained only the essentials, such as radios for communication, a life-support system, instrumentation and an ejection seat. The service module attached to the cabin carried chemical batteries, the retro system, support equipment and orientation rockets. Upon re-entry to Earth, this service module was separated from the main cabin.

To be launched into orbit, the ship was aided by an R-7 booster rocket. This was the world's first intercontinental ballistic missile. Somewhat poetically, it was originally developed to carry nuclear bombs, but eventually ended up carrying a human into outer space. Tereshkova's SK-2 spacesuit was very similar to the one worn by Yuri Gagarin; however, it was modified for a female. Unlike the classic Moon-landing suits it was only designed to be pressurised in the event of the cabin pressure being lost, and to aid in the parachute landing, and was not designed for space walking. Comfort, however, was not factored into the equation at all, making for a cramped and painful flight for the intergalactic adventurer.

"She had to be not only a pilot, but also an engineer, a doctor and a navigator, and it required a gruelling training schedule"

to Earth. Applicants were also required to be under 30 years of age, under 70 kilograms in weight and under 170 centimetres (five-and-a-half feet) tall. The woman from Maslennikovo ticked all the boxes.

Tereshkova's world transformed overnight. Along with the three other women, she underwent 18 months of intense training. All these women were burning with desire and ambition to go into space, but none of them were pilots. Whereas in modern spaceflight, where each crew is comprised of specialists, the cosmonauts of these earliest days of space travel were expected to fulfil all roles.

Tereshkova had to be not only a pilot, but also an engineer, a doctor and a navigator, and it required a gruelling training schedule. Tereshkova underwent weightless and centrifuge tests, was trained in rocket theory and spacecraft engineering and had pilot training in MiG-15UTI jet fighters, along with parachute jump after parachute jump. To prepare herself for the solitude of space travel, she spent hours alone in a silent chamber. The women underwent examinations to ensure they were prepared for the rigorous demands of a flight into outer space.

The boots on Tereshkova's spacesuit were specially designed for her parachute landing

Tereshkova and Gagarin both became powerful tools for the Soviet Union to use to send a strong message

worked quickly to develop a new landing algorithm. However, upon parachuting out of her craft, Tereshkova realised that, to her horror, she was heading towards a large lake. Due to her sickness and exhaustion she worried she would not have the energy to swim. Luckily she was blown away from the water by a high wind, but did receive a heavy landing as a result, which left her bruised and a little worse for the wear – but thankfully alive.

Aching and exhausted she may have been, but Tereshkova was soon hailed with the title of Hero of the Soviet Union. She also received the Order of Lenin and Gold Star Medal. Tereshkova was, essentially, an overnight legend. Although Tereshkova herself was delighted with her achievements, there are questions over the USSR's true motivations for putting her in space in the first place. Tereshkova was, to them, the perfect candidate. Her father was a war hero, she had a strong proletarian background, came from humble origins and was a diligent student and worker. She was, in no small way, a communist dream made real. Sergei Korolev, principal designer of the Soviet space programme, admitted that although some others were better prepared than Tereshkova for the trip, she was chosen due to her ability to influence crowds, arouse sympathy and be an enticing spokesperson. Tereshkova was very eager to fly again after her world-record-breaking flight, but just like Gagarin before her, she was considered too powerful a propaganda tool to risk. Tereshkova's image was used to emphasise the strength and success of the Soviet space programme. Her face was put on stamps, her image immortalised in monuments.

Like Gagarin, Tereshkova's public image was controlled and dictated. But while he was the military hero, she was the soft, feminine, peaceful civilian, dressed with immaculate hair, dresses, high

After months of training, finally Tereshkova was ready to achieve her dream. Originally it was planned that she would launch in Vostok 5, with her fellow trainee Valentina Ponomaryova following her in Vostok 6, as the two highest achievers. However, plans changed. It was later decided a male cosmonaut would fly in Vostok 5, and Tereshkova would conduct a solo mission in Vostok 6. Tereshkova had been picked from all the female candidates to undergo the monumental flight, and she was aged just 26 years old.

On the morning of 16 June 1963, Tereshkova prepared herself for the historic flight. She dressed in her spacesuit and, not willing to be outdone by her male counterparts, followed the tradition of urinating on the tyre of the bus that picked her up to transport her to the launch pad. Another first for female cosmonauts. She was sealed inside the spacecraft and waited there during a two-hour-long countdown. Finally the ambitious girl from the textile factory was launched into space. Her call sign was Chaika, or 'Seagull', which she yelled in jubilation as she made history.

Despite her monumental achievement, the flight was not exactly a comfortable one for Tereshkova. She experienced severe nausea along with physical discomfort in the tiny ship. Her sickness was not due to motion, but due to the terrible quality of food she

was given. She was also ordered to remain strapped into her seat, but this resulted in cramp in her leg, which she described as 'intolerable', as well as a rash and itch that couldn't be scratched. Despite this she spent three days in space and orbited the Earth 48 times. This single flight amounted to more flight time than all the American astronauts combined. The mission provided valuable data concerning the effects spaceflight had on the female body, and Tereshkova also maintained a flight log. She took photographs of the horizon, which were later used to help identify aerosol layers in the atmosphere. She also manually oriented the spacecraft. While on board, live television was broadcast from the craft, and Tereshkova even spoke with Premier Nikita Khrushchev via a camera. When Vostok 6 was launched, the two vessels came within 4.9 kilometres (three miles) of each other in orbit, and the two cosmonauts exchanged communications via radio.

With over 70 hours logged in space, the mission was an apparent success. However, there were complications that were covered up for almost 40 years that Tereshkova was forbidden to speak of. An error in the ship's navigation software caused the craft to move away from Earth. This sounds minor, but could have ended in tragedy and disaster for Tereshkova. Luckily the skilled cosmonaut recognised the error and reported it. Soviet scientists

"She experienced severe nausea along with physical discomfort"

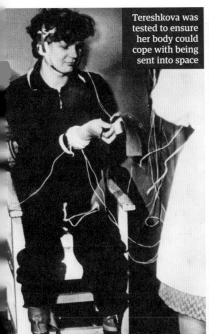

Tereshkova was tested to ensure her body could cope with being sent into space

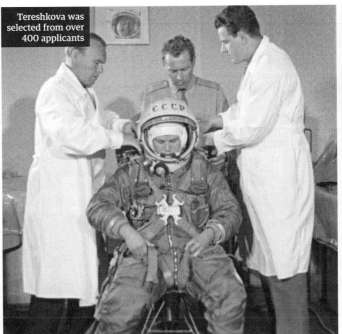

Tereshkova was selected from over 400 applicants

Tereshkova shortly after her landing, some bruising is visible on her head

Women of space

Tereshkova blazed a trail through space for an array of ambitious and incredible women to follow

Sally Ride

Born in LA, Ride originally pursued a career in professional tennis, but then went on to study science, obtaining a doctorate in physics in 1978. Beating out thousands of applicants, Ride was chosen to be one of six of NASA's first female astronauts that same year. She first worked as a capsule communicator, but aged 32 underwent her first spaceflight as a mission specialist aboard the Challenger. Ride was the first woman to operate the shuttle's robotic arm. Ride also went on to be the first American woman to go into space twice, with a further mission aboard the Challenger. Ride later dedicated her time to encouraging girls to embrace the study of science.

Kalpana Chawla

Born in Karnal, India, Chawla obtained a degree in aeronautical engineering before immigrating to the United States in the 1980s. She continued her studies at the University of Colorado, where she earned a doctorate in 1988. That year she began working for NASA's Ames Research Center. In 1994 she was selected as a candidate to become an astronaut, and her first opportunity to be launched into space came aboard the Columbia in 1997. Chawla made history with this flight as the first Indian-born woman in space. However, her story was tragically cut short when, during the landing of her second shuttle, disaster struck and the ship depressurised, killing all crew on board.

Anousheh Ansari

Ansari is an Iranian-born engineer who immigrated to the United States in 1984. She achieved a master's degree in electrical engineering and computer science at George Mason University. In 1993 she co-founded Telecom Technologies Inc. with her husband and brother-in-law, then went on to also co-found Prodea Systems, a technology and services management company. Ansari made a huge donation to the XPrize foundation and became a spokeswoman for the privatisation of space. In 2006, aged 40, she became the first Muslim woman in space and the first self-funded woman to fly to the International Space Station. She describes herself not as a 'space tourist', but instead a 'spaceflight participant'.

Yi So-yeon

Yi was born and raised in Gwangju, South Korea and earned bachelor's and master's degrees at KAIST, going on to become an engineering physics professor. Yi was chosen as one of two finalists in the Korean Astronaut Program, a South Korean initiative to send the first Korean into space via the Russian space programme. Yi was launched into space in 2008 at an estimated cost of $20 million. Although officially recognised as a spaceflight participant, Yi was involved in many scientific experiments while onboard, such as monitoring the effect spaceflight had on 1,000 fruit flies. Yi experienced a traumatic landing, with the crew subjected to ten-times the normal gravitational forces of Earth.

Helen Sharman

Born in Sheffield, Sharman achieved a bachelor's in science from the University of Sheffield and a PhD from Birkbeck, University of London. She went on to work as a research and development technologist. However, her life changed when she answered a radio advertisement seeking applicants to become the first British astronaut. On 15 November 1989 she was selected live on ITV, beating out 13,000 other applicants. The project was known as Project Juno, a joint Soviet Union-British mission. Sharman received 18 months of intense training for her flight before she was launched into space on 18 May 1991. The Soyuz TM-12 mission lasted eight days, during which Sharman conducted medical and agricultural tests.

Svetlana Savitskaya

Savitskaya was born in Moscow in 1948 as the daughter of a famous WWII fighter pilot. She wished to follow in his footsteps, but her air force application was denied due to her age. Instead she took on parachuting, completing 450 jumps before the age of 18. She then began competing for the Soviet National Aerobatics team and achieved a master's in flight engineering. She joined the cosmonaut training programme in 1980 and was launched in 1982 as the second woman in space. Not satisfied with second best, she went on to become the first woman to fly to space twice in 1984, and the first woman to perform a spacewalk. When she arrived at the space station, she was handed an apron and jokingly told to get in the kitchen.

heels and make-up. Even her marriage to fellow cosmonaut Andriyan Nikolayev seemed perfectly crafted to fit the Soviet narrative, but Tereshkova denies that this was arranged. Although many believed that Tereshkova's accomplishment was proof of gender equality under communism, it is very difficult to ignore the fact that it took 19 more years for another Soviet woman to be sent into space. Female participation in the Soviet space programme seemed to be yet another way to beat the United States, and to create positive PR.

Indeed, after Tereshkova's flight, several members of the Soviet Air Force immediately attempted to discredit her achievements. Accusations ranged from her being drunk at the launch pad to being insubordinate in orbit, ignoring direct orders and becoming overly emotional. There was particular bad blood around her pointing out the incorrect spacecraft orientation, a concept which is difficult to grapple with, as not pointing it out would have resulted in almost certain death for Tereshkova, who clearly chose to prioritise her own life over the embarrassment of her male colleagues. Tereshkova

Tereshkova and Nikolayev were married in 1963

Valery and Tereshkova both became beloved figures in their country after their flights

President Putin congratulated Tereshkova upon her 80th birthday

Tereshkova reportedly ended up vomiting because of the terrible food she was supplied with on her mission

A Russian doll was even made to celebrate Tereshkova's achievement

Tereshkova was subjected to an intense training period to prepare her for spaceflight

herself denies the claims that she was difficult or psychologically unstable. Cosmonaut chief Nikolai Kamanin agreed with Tereshkova, saying she was never tired, never objected and did all she could to complete the flight programme. Ultimately, Tereshkova's objectors were discredited.

The PR programme behind Tereshkova worked spectacularly well. She became an instant celebrity, travelling the world as a cultural ambassador and spokeswoman. One of the most surprising impacts of her fame was within the United States. The Americans of the Cold War had a very definitive image of what a Soviet woman was - miserable, shabby, wearing terrible clothes, faces without make-up and generally suffering under their government. However, Tereshkova's image directly challenged this. She was a successful female in the world of science but, predictably, the US media focused on her sex appeal, dubbing her 'the Russian blonde in space' - a confusing nickname considering the fact that Tereshkova was a brunette.

However, her success also forced the US to acknowledge that they would also have to tap into their own womens' talents and open up the male-dominated world of science to them, especially if

"She was a successful female in the world of science"

they wished to win the Space Race. Tereshkova caused ripples in the US, with female pilots in full support of her and inspired by her achievements, while some more conservative members of NASA and the US Air Force compared her to the chimps that had been sent to orbit. One NASA spokesperson said the thought of putting women in space made him sick to his stomach. Although Tereshkova challenged American expectations of women, the sexism in the country was a near-insurmountable barrier, and it would take another two decades for an American woman to be sent into space.

Tereshkova herself struggled with the expectations and hero worship she was subjected to. She had always been an ambitious woman, but she never wished to be famous or adored. She certainly didn't want to be hounded by the press. She was subjected to a gruelling schedule where all of her behavior and image was carefully controlled. She could no longer enjoy a private life, and this impacted on her relationship with her husband. Although they had a daughter in 1964 - the first child born to parents who had both been in space - the relationship was strained, and neither of them were happy. However, divorce would mean PR suicide, so the two remained together as a 'happy space family' until 1982.

Although Tereshkova had to deal with the fact she was unlikely to ever be sent into space again, she was not ready to surrender to the life of a Soviet housewife. She became a member of the Supreme Soviet of the Soviet Union and studied at the Zkukovsky Air Force Academy, graduating as a cosmonaut engineer and later earning a doctorate in engineering. She went on to become a prominent member of the Communist Party and represented

Tereshkova presented a badge to Neil Armstrong in memory of his visit to the Gagarin Training Center

the nation abroad in numerous international events. Her memberships and accolades included becoming a member of the World Peace Council, achieving the rank of deputy to the Supreme Soviet and being the recipient of numerous prestigious awards.

After the collapse of the Soviet Union Tereshkova lost her political office, but her legendary status did not falter. Today, although somewhat of a forgotten hero in the West, in her homeland she is hailed as a legend, surpassed only by Yuri Gagarin and Alexei Leonov. She was elected to the State Duma where she continues to serve to this day, and carried the Olympic torch in 2008. Upon her 80th birthday she was invited to meet with Vladimir Putin in his residence. It seems age has done little to slow down her thirst for adventure, as she recently said she would like to fly to Mars, even if it was to be a one-way trip.

Gemini 8:
Mission abort

From successfully docking two crafts in space
to a horrifying, stomach-turning problem...

Neil Armstrong was the first person to walk on the Moon, but Apollo 11 in 1969 was not his first foray into space. On 16 March 1966, NASA launched the two-man, three-day Gemini 8 mission from Cape Kennedy (now Cape Canaveral). Armstrong was the commander and, together with David Scott, spent more than six hours performing nine manoeuvres to rendezvous with the unmanned Gemini Agena Target Vehicle, which launched earlier in the day.

Having completed the first ever successful docking in orbit of two vehicles, control of Gemini 8 was transferred to Agena. At this point, Scott should have begun preparing for an extravehicular activity (EVA) to retrieve a nuclear radiation experiment from the front of Gemini's spacecraft adapter and in order to activate a micrometeoroid experiment on the Agena. Instead,

however, disaster struck within just 30 minutes of Gemini 8 docking with the Agena Target Vehicle.

The combined spacecraft had veered 30 degrees off the horizon and couldn't be corrected. A malfunctioning thruster sent the vehicle violently tumbling and twisting around its vertical axis. When control was returned to Gemini, it yawed, rolled and pitched, faster and faster. Even as Gemini was disengaged, it revolved once every second.

With the crew in danger of blacking out, the mission was aborted and the re-entry system activated. This stabilised the spacecraft and allowed Gemini to land in the sea 1,000 kilometres (621 miles) south of Yokosuka in Japan. It was a disappointment that the mission had to be aborted, but at least - ten hours and 44 minutes after launch - Armstrong and Scott were safely back on Earth.

An image taken just 0.6 metres (two feet) away from the first ever docking of two spacecraft - Gemini 8 and Agena

Neil Armstrong and David Scott await the recovery ship following splashdown of Gemini 8, after the mission was aborted

©NASA

INTERVIEW BIO

Margaret Hamilton

Margaret Hamilton was a computer scientist and software engineer during the Apollo era. She joined the Charles Stark Draper Laboratory - now known as Draper - at the Massachusetts Institute of Technology (MIT) in 1964. From there she helped develop the on-board flight software as was given the role of lead programmer on the Apollo Guidance Computer (AGC). The AGC was a pivotal part of the Apollo spacecraft, and the mission simply wouldn't have been possible without the diligent work of Hamilton. This earned her Presidential Medal of Freedom in 2016, awarded by Barack Obama.

© Getty

The software genius behind the moon landings

Margaret Hamilton reveals the inside story of the Apollo program and how sacrifice, hard work and constant questioning led to the completion of arguably humankind's greatest ever adventure

Interviewed by Lee Cavendish

What was a day in the life of a NASA computer scientist like during the 1960s?

On the unmanned missions I began writing software mostly in the system software area. We had a lot to do with error detection recovery. My first piece of programming, which we now refer to as 'software engineering computer science', or some combination there of, had to do with error detection recovery, because they were worried about unmanned mission aborts - we needed the post-mortem software.

So they [Draper management] thought, 'We're going to give it to Margaret, because she's a beginner and it doesn't matter if she screws up because that means the mission is aborted anyway, so no big deal'. So I wrote the abort program and I called it 'Forget It', because if it didn't work, it went to post-mortem. Then wouldn't you know, the very next unmanned mission aborted, and it went to this program called 'Forget It'. That made an impact on me, even though the people on the project, the engineer guys and everything, said we would never abort because everything was going to run perfectly. That's when I learned that, when they say it's never going to happen, I shouldn't believe them, and I always said 'what if it happens'.

After the unmanned missions I worked on the systems software, which had to do with the software that affected all the people working on it. So if you made a mistake, it affected everybody with this software. After that, when the manned missions started, I took over - I was the lead - the manned software, which involved the Command Module, the Lunar Module and the systems software shared between them. The big challenge was that it had to be 'man-rated'. So now I started worrying about errors even more than I did back in the old days on the unmanned missions. What 'man-rated' meant from a software perspective was that the software system itself, with all the code, could have no errors. You couldn't have any errors, including data conflicts, timing conflicts and priority conflicts, and also included error detection and recovery in real-time when it was running.

Anyway, it had all to do with software and systems. Software interfacing with other software, software interfacing with hardware to astronaut-ware and whatever other -wares there were around to interface to!

When you talk about the software for aborting the mission, would this have been used for the famous moment where Neil Armstrong and Buzz Aldrin were running out of fuel when they managed to land on the Moon?

That's what I worked on more than just about anything. But yes, that's a mission where I have many memories about the putting together: why it was put together, what led up to it, how it was put together, what it did and how it affected the mission.

What were the alarms going off before the landing and what were you doing when they were going off?

Well, one 'what if' I had was, what if there's an emergency during the mission and there was no way to tell the astronauts about it. The hardware could know, the software could know, but what about the astronauts? They should know if an emergency is going to happen. That was my main worry a couple of years before I put together the software. I wanted to bring up the problem to the hardware guys and the mission guys, but first they were going to say, "How are you going to solve it?"

I held a meeting with the hardware guys first and told them the problem and how I would solve it, and these were higher-ups. One of the hardware guys said, "Yeah, but there's one problem." I said, "What's that?" Then he said, "You can't talk to the astronauts unless the DSKY [Display Keyboard] is on." They said, "Let us think about it for a couple of days and we'll come back to it." They came back a couple of days later and said they were going to do it, and they were going to keep it on all the time so that the software can interface to the astronauts.

What it needed to do was, where the software was asynchronous - higher priority things could interrupt other priority things - the communication at the time was synchronous with the astronaut. If the software wanted to interrupt the astronaut it had to be an asynchronous system with the astronauts, with the two systems in parallel.

Then along came mission experts, hardware experts that said, "Yeah, we see what you're doing, but it's never been done before and it can't be done. It's one of the biggest problems with distributed processing." So I asked them what the problem would be, and they described the problem to me and I'll refer back to it, but I went home that night and I thought after I had gone through all this, I don't not dare to do this.

I came back the next day and I described the solution and they said, "Yeah, that would work." So we were running often with support from the hardware, support from the people that trained the astronauts and mission control. A big hurdle was to know that you weren't going to have the man-rated requirement compromise.

So then, back to the present in the past, when this happened just before the landing there was an emergency, and the priority displays noticed that it was one of the never-supposed-to-happen alarms that came up. In this case a 1202 and a 1201 alarm came up, and it was one of those never-supposed-to-happen alarms.

Meantime, back in the Mission Control area, prior to the mission the astronauts were in simulations practising before the landing. They were practising with Jack Garman, who was the software counterpart at Mission Control. When they were practising, Aldrin would hurry through and get to the landing, because that's what he wanted to practise. So he kept practising and noticed that if you put the rendezvous radar switch in a certain position that would help get quickly through to landing, but then what happens is if you forget to put the switch back, the 1202 and 1201 alarms would come up.

That happened a few times; sometimes it didn't happen. So they knew what caused those alarms and they were familiar with it if they saw an emergency 1202 or 1201 alarm. The astronauts recognised it and Jack Garman recognised it, as he practised with them a lot.

Now keep in mind the astronaut actually created the mistake, but it was interesting that we were warning the astronaut because he was the one that could fix that mistake, ironically.

Going on at the same time at Mission Control, the bosses were saying to Jack, "What do we do?!" And Jack noticed, "Oh, okay. It's a 1202 and a 1201. We know what to do. We take off the switch and put it back to where it belongs." And they weren't worried and depending on Jack, as he understood being a user of the software, as did Aldrin.

Where were you when this was unfolding?
In the SCAMA [MIT's System Control and Monitoring Arrangement] room.

What was going through your mind?
Well, I'd like to lighten it a little bit, but it was sheer panic [laughs]. I didn't know whether to be worried about the astronauts or the software!

What's the story regarding your daughter and how she found a problem in the software?
Well, Lauren is her name, and we're talking about Apollo 8. I would take her to work with me, often on nights and weekends – not during the normal hours. Well, no one back then had normal hours! But we actually simulated stuff in a digital way, but also hardware; we had the hardware just like the astronauts had.

I was practising with the hardware simulation one time when I took her to work and she wanted to play astronaut. So she went over and started playing, thinking she was doing what I did, and all of a sudden the system crashed. On her own, playing around, she got the mission started and then she started playing around again, and she was in mid-course in the mission, on the way to the Moon, and then she hit some other keys which selected the prelaunch program, which then wiped out all the navigation data mid-course.

She didn't know what she was doing. When I saw what happened I said, "Oh my god, this could happen with the astronauts. They could do the same thing." Keeping in mind, mission phases

Above: The famous image of Hamilton standing next to the code that would take humans to the Moon

Below left: The Apollo Guidance Computer (AGC) and the Display Keyboard (DSKY)

Below right: Hamilton gave legitimacy to having 'software engineering' as its own discipline in science

Right (clockwise): Buzz Aldrin during the Apollo 11 mission to the lunar surface

The work of Hamilton and the rest of the Draper team were instrumental in getting humans to the Moon

Jim Lovell on the Apollo 8 mission, during which he made the almost-critical 'Lauren error'

[in the software] could not share. There was not enough room in the computer's software, so when they shared it was a big no-no and knocked out the navigation system.

I went back to the higher-ups at MIT and NASA and I said, "What if the astronauts did the same thing?" "Never would happen," they said. Just like that. "Forget it. Never would happen." So I said, "What if it happens?" "No, it won't happen. They [the astronauts] are too well trained. It's not going to happen." I said I wanted to put a change in to prevent an astronaut from doing that. They said, "No, you can't do that." So I said, "Well, can I at least put in a program note - which was a formal spec that goes with that - and say 'do not select P01 during flight.'" Which was yet another one that caused laughter among everybody, because it was funny. Why would anyone select prelaunch while they're in flight? The astronaut knows better.

Well, wouldn't you know that the very next flight, Apollo 8, [Jim] Lovell did exactly that, what we call the 'Lauren error'. And I remember being in the SCAMA room, and the guys were there and they were wondering what's going on. I remember saying it's the Lauren error. Just after the flight they said, "You can put that change in now if you want."

Was it the physical space constraints that made putting that small bit of code in hard?
Yes, absolutely. That had problems of its own. That's the reason why we rolled mission phases in and out,

"When the alarms came up, I knew this wasn't supposed to be happening, and I also recognised the software"

but that caused errors, and we tried to force fit stuff in there, but that again caused errors. We also had asynchronous, and then we'd have errors because things would be interrupting, and then how do you know it's going to happen safely. We had a lot of knowledge about errors, having those constraints.

How hard was it to create software that astronauts could understand and control?
That was part of it, the other part was having it man-rated and trying to make it fit. Many problems existed with that which people don't have to contend with now, but they have other problems. They have so much room; they can make all kinds of errors and make it a more complex system of errors.

But how hard was it? The priority display, that was the first time that kind of interaction had taken place, and also the first time that a distributed environment had to be set into place. At the time it wasn't hard because we didn't know any better. We just did what we thought had to be done. You just solved it because you just could not fail, not because of your management, or NASA or whatever, but

because we all had the attitude we can't fail. It has to be right.

What were your initial thoughts as Neil Armstrong and Buzz Aldrin took their first steps on the Moon?
Well, I was there [in the SCAMA room] as one of the people that were required because it was going through the things it was going through. But when the 1202 and 1201 alarms came up, I knew this wasn't supposed to be happening, and I also recognised the software. My reaction was, "Why didn't it happen before this? Why now, during the first mission to land on the Moon?" But at the same time I had confidence in the software, and so I just thought it is what it is. You've just got to get through it and in fact it worked out.

When it landed it was maybe the most exciting moment of my life. Because in a sense everything came rushing through my mind, what with the background and getting to that point, it was an interesting feeling of what the software was doing, how we got there, the things we went through to get there. But all of that just came in a rush.

Fire in the cockpit

A catastrophic flash fire killed three astronauts and nearly ended the Apollo programme that was intended to reach the Moon

Reaching the Moon was the raison d'etre for NASA, and America's space agency raced headlong toward that goal. AS-204, the first manned mission of the Apollo program, was scheduled for liftoff on 21 February 1967, intended to take three astronauts into orbit.

Now, after preliminary work in the Mercury and Gemini programs, Apollo would eventually take mankind to the Moon, as President John F Kennedy had challenged the nation to accomplish before the end of the 1960s. On 27 January 1967, however, AS-204 came to grief. Three astronauts died in a tragic fire at Launch Complex 34 in Cape Canaveral, Florida. The accident occurred during a 'plugs out integrated test' of systems and procedures operating as nearly as possible to actual flight conditions, including a simulated launch.

The three astronauts, command pilot Virgil I 'Gus' Grissom, age 40, senior pilot Ed White, 36, and pilot Roger B Chaffee, 31, perished inside the command module within 30 seconds of the first indication of

fire, due to smoke inhalation and burns. Training for his third mission, Grissom, an Air Force lieutenant colonel, had participated in the Mercury and Gemini programmes. White, also an Air Force lieutenant colonel, had piloted Gemini 4, becoming the first American to walk in space. Chaffee, a US Navy lieutenant commander, was anticipating the experience of his first space flight.

Prior to the test date, the astronauts themselves had noted concerns regarding the readiness of the command module. During a meeting in August 1966, the crew had expressed misgivings about the copious amount of flammable material in the cockpit to aerospace engineer Joseph F Shea, the Apollo Spacecraft Program Office manager. Shea ordered the flammable materials removed but did not personally supervise the operation. At the time of the accident, both adhesive Velcro and nylon netting were present in command/service module CM-012. Shea deemed the spacecraft safe, but the crew posed for a photograph with their hands clasped and heads bowed in prayer. The accompanying inscription read: "It isn't that we don't trust you, Joe, but this time we've decided to go over your head."

Grissom's frustration grew steadily, and during a visit to his home in Texas five days before the tragedy he pulled a lemon from a tree in his backyard. When he returned to Cape Canaveral, he hung the lemon from the flight simulator in an obvious display of mockery. The spacecraft constructed by contractor North American Aviation had actually been delivered to Cape Canaveral on 26 August 1966, with 113 major engineering changes due for completion after arrival. Another 623 necessary engineering modifications were identified and completed following delivery.

At 1pm on 27 January 1967, the crew entered the command module and took positions in the capsule atop the Saturn 1B rocket, which was not fuelled for the test. The test itself was not considered to be hazardous.

Immediately, Grissom noticed an odour he described as similar to "sour buttermilk" in the air circulating through his pressure suit. An investigation caused a delay of an hour

The command module for the ill-fated mission arrives at Kennedy Space Center in August 1966

and 12 minutes. The issue was later determined to be unrelated to the fatal fire. Meanwhile, communications problems due to a continuously live microphone that could not be turned off caused additional delays. At approximately 6:30pm, Grissom remarked, "How are we going to get to the Moon if we can't talk between three buildings?" Another crewmember noted, "They can't hear a word you're saying!" Grissom repeated the comment as his dissatisfaction increased.

One minute later, a surge in the spacecraft's AC Bus 2 voltage (alternating current voltage) readings occurred, probably indicating a short circuit in a bundle of wiring. Moments later, one of the crewmen, probably Chaffee, said something like "Flames!" Within two seconds, White said, "We've got fire in the cockpit." Witnesses viewing the closed circuit television feed of the hatch window reported that the flames, accelerated by the 100 per cent oxygen atmosphere and combustible materials, spread swiftly from left to right.

Nearly seven seconds passed before the final communication from the command module was heard. It was probably White who cried out, in a garbled transmission, something to the effect

Grissom, White and Chaffee in front of the launch pad where, sadly, all three would perish

"It isn't that we don't trust you, Joe, but this time we've decided to go over your head"

of "We've got a bad fire! Let's get out! We're burning up!" Seventeen seconds elapsed from the first indication of fire to the interruption of communications. By this time the command module hull had ruptured.

Emergency procedures called for White to open the hatch; however, interior pressure that was higher than external atmospheric pressure made this impossible. Opening it from outside required the use of ratchets and could be accomplished in about 90 seconds in normal circumstances, but thick, black smoke and flames billowed throughout the immediate area, preventing ground personnel from completing the task for five minutes.

The Apollo program was suspended as a NASA review board examined the evidence available and concluded that six conditions had contributed to the disaster: a sealed cabin pressurised with an oxygen atmosphere; an extensive distribution of combustible materials in the cabin; vulnerable wiring carrying spacecraft power; vulnerable plumbing carrying a combustible corrosive coolant; inadequate provisions for the crew to escape; and inadequate provisions for rescue or medical assistance. NASA engineers, North American Aviation, and others had failed to give adequate attention to aspects of the program they considered "routine". They had evaluated the possibility

of catastrophic fire in space but never fully contemplated such an event while the spacecraft was still on the ground. The US Senate and House of Representatives each conducted inquiries into the disaster as well.

As a result of the awful ultimate sacrifice made by the three astronauts, numerous design modifications were completed in subsequent Apollo spacecraft. Lessons had been learned at a great cost. AS-204 was renamed Apollo 1 in honour of the crew, and their bravery is recalled annually during a Day of Remembrance. An exhibit honouring Grissom, White, and Chaffee opened at the Kennedy Space Center in 2017.

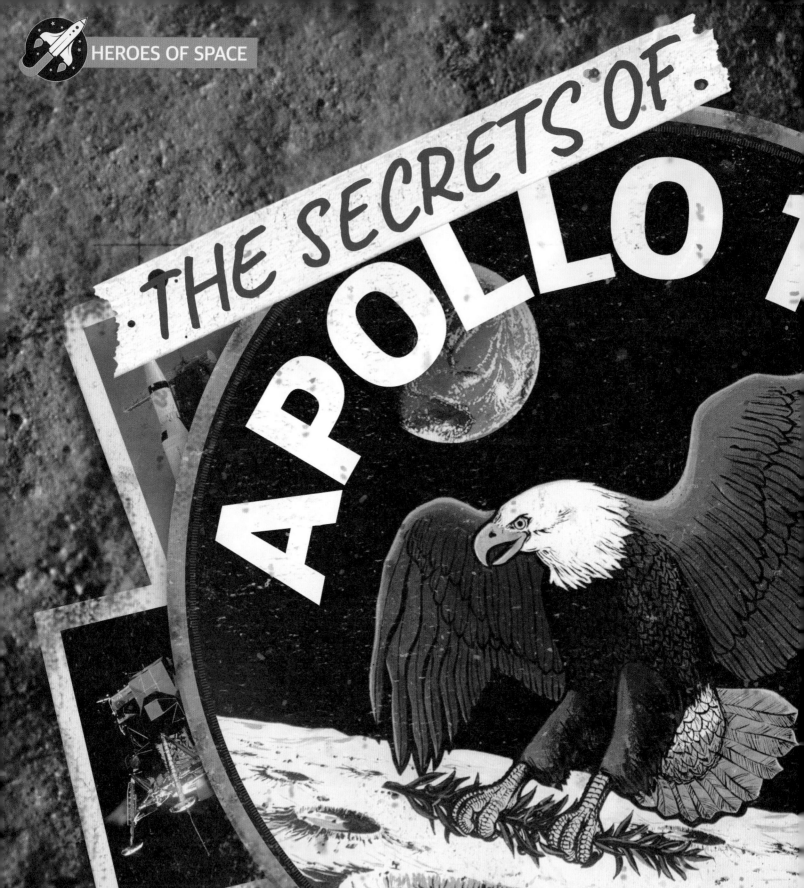

THE SECRETS OF APOLLO 1

Buzz Aldrin & the last cr

unpublished archives of t

Over 50 years ago, humankind achieved one of the greatest technical feats of all time. Less than nine years after President Kennedy had set the goal of landing a man on the surface of the Moon and returning him safely to Earth, NASA achieved that most astonishing aim on 20 July 1969.

Those intervening years had been a white-knuckle ride. Beginning with Alan Shepard's 15-minute suborbital Mercury flight in 1961, NASA progressed through a series of milestones in their mission to reach the Moon. There was the loss of a Mercury capsule and the near-drowning of its pilot Gus Grissom; John Glenn's re-entry with a retrorocket still attached to his Friendship 7 capsule; a slew of hugely successful Gemini missions, including one that almost span out of control, potentially threatening the life of the astronaut who in 1969 would take that first historic step and then four fully flown Apollo missions: two in low-Earth orbit, two that orbited the Moon and only one to test the full system. NASA had to endure the catastrophic loss of Grissom and his two crew mates, Edward White and Roger Chaffee, in 1967 in Apollo 1's tragic fire on the launch pad, but the space agency had resolved to carry on, completely redesigning the Lunar Command Module and carrying out major changes to the Lunar Landing Module - the LEM as it was known - in that short space of time.

"A space mission will never be routine. You're putting three humans on top of an enormous amount of high explosive" Gene Kranz

Amid triumph and tragedy, on 16 July 1969 NASA was ready to go to the Moon. Yet the trials and tribulations of the previous years were not over, and the three-man crew of Apollo 11 - Neil Armstrong, Buzz Aldrin and Michael Collins - were facing one of the most dramatic spaceflights in history. We recall the historic first words said on the lunar surface and the elation of the largest TV audience in history at that time when they saw those grainy black-and-white images from the Moon, but there is so much more to the story of Apollo 11 that may not be as well known.

Their first task, of course, was to leave Earth on top of the mighty Saturn V rocket - the tallest, most powerful rocket ever built. Many astronauts who were propelled into space by the Saturn V describe it as being a very smooth ride. Neil Armstrong is quoted as saying that while the launch for all those watching on Cocoa Beach or at Cape Canaveral was deafening, the crew could only detect a slight increase in background noise,

mbers reveal the

59 Moon landing

No escape plan: what NASA didn't want the astronauts to know

A secret launch document revealed that an escape plan - should the Saturn V rocket fail - was bogus

What the astronauts were told

The crew were told that should the leak cause an engine to fail at liftoff, their capsule would eject to safety far away from the failing, exploding rocket. To their knowledge, Armstrong and his crew had been sufficiently trained to escape.

What would have happened

Apollo 11 would not be saved if something had gone wrong in the first two minutes after liftoff. The abort system needed two seconds after detection of a catastrophic failure to activate the launch escape system. If an engine were to go out on the first stage, within half a second the Saturn V would have broken up and killed the crew.

a lot of shaking and feeling akin to being on board a large jet aeroplane on takeoff. Yet as smooth a ride as it was, being on top of that much rocket fuel was always a dangerous experience. "A space mission will never be routine because you're putting three humans on top of an enormous amount of high explosive," Gene Kranz, flight director for Apollo 11's lunar landing, told us. If there were any nerves, the astronauts weren't feeling it, according to Buzz Aldrin. "We felt that our survival was in the probability of 99 per cent. There were a lot of risks involved but there were a lot of points to abort the mission short of continuing on something risky."

Once in space the Command Service Module had to rotate and dock with the Lunar Module, which was embedded in the final S-IVB stage of the Saturn V rocket. After the two spacecraft had mated, onwards they flew to the Moon, leaving the S-IVB stage trailing in space behind them. Some time later, the crew spotted something strange outside: a light that appeared to be following them. When Michael Collins used the onboard telescope to view it, he couldn't make it out - it looked like a series of ellipses, and when focusing the telescope it seemed L-shaped, but that could have just been the way sunlight was glinting off it.

Reticent to tell mission control in Houston, Texas, that they were being raced to the Moon by a UFO, the crew cautiously asked where the SIVB rocket

stage was. "A few moments later they came back to us and said it was around 6,000 miles [9,656 kilometres] away," recalled Aldrin. "We really didn't think we were looking at something that far away, so we decided to go to sleep and not talk about it anymore." Aldrin doesn't believe it was an alien spaceship, but that it was more likely the Sun reflecting off one of four metal panels that fell away from the rocket stage when they docked with the Lunar Module. For almost four days Apollo 11 flew towards the Moon, where Armstrong and Aldrin climbed into the Lunar Module - the 'Eagle' - and said goodbye to Collins, who was to remain in the Command Module in orbit around the Moon.

As the Eagle flew around the far side of the Moon, things in mission control were growing tense. "There was a degree of seriousness in mission control that I hadn't even seen in training," said Kranz. "That was when you realised this was the real deal: today, we land on the Moon." Almost immediately after separating from the Command Module there were problems. Radio communication with the Eagle was sketchy at best, and they were coming up to the point where the landing could no longer be aborted if something was wrong.

"It was up to me to decide if we had enough information to make the go/no-go [decision] and continue the descent to the Moon," said Kranz. So, five minutes before the powered descent to the

"There was a degree of seriousness in mission control that I hadn't even seen in training"

Gene Kranz

Left: The Apollo 11 crew 'suit up' for a countdown demonstration test

Right top: The huge Saturn V rocket carries three men towards the Moon

Right bottom: In his spacesuit, Neil Armstrong practises getting back to the first rung of the ladder on the Lunar Module

To: H. R. Haldeman
From: Bill Safire

July 18, 1969

IN EVENT OF MOON DISASTER:

Fate has ordained that the men who went to the Moon to explore in peace will stay on the Moon to rest in peace.

These brave men, Neil Armstrong and Edwin Aldrin, know that there is no hope for their recovery. But they also know that there is hope for mankind in their sacrifice.

These two men are laying down their lives in mankind's most noble goal: the search for truth and understanding.

They will be mourned by their families and friends; they will be mourned by the nation; they will be mourned by the people of the world; they will be mourned by a Mother Earth that dared send two of her sons into the unknown.

In their exploration, they stirred the people of the world to feel as one; in their sacrifice, they bind more tightly the brotherhood of man.

In ancient days, men looked at the stars and saw their heroes in the constellations. In modern times, we do much the same, but our heroes are epic men of flesh and blood.

Others will follow, and surely find their way home. Man's search will not be denied. But these men were the first, and they will remain the foremost in our hearts.

For every human being who looks up at the Moon in the nights to come will know that there is some corner of another world that is forever mankind.

PRIOR TO THE PRESIDENT'S STATEMENT:

The president should telephone each of the widows-to-be.

AFTER THE PRESIDENT'S STATEMENT, AT THE POINT WHEN NASA ENDS COMMUNICATIONS WITH THE MEN:

A clergyman should adopt the same procedure as a burial at sea, commending their souls to "the deepest of the deep", concluding with the Lord's Prayer.

lunar surface was due to begin, with radio communication cutting in and out, Kranz asked his flight controllers to give him their go/no-go based on the last frame of data that they saw. They all said "go." And then things turned from bad to nearly catastrophic. The spacecraft's guidance computer, developed at MIT under the auspices of Charles Draper - the lab at MIT now bears his name - was a 2MHz system that was the first in the world to use integrated circuits. Its fixed memory was an ingeniously designed 'Core Rope' which consisted of a set of small hoops. 'Little Old Ladies', as it was referred to at the time, along with machines would thread the code either through or around the hoops to give the computer its 1 or 0 value. If the MIT code was threaded incorrectly, the 'programmer' would have to laboriously go through the woven cores and debug it. When the crew were approaching the Moon for the landing, various alarms were triggered by the computer. "Whatever information we were looking at [disappeared] and

Mission control loses contact with Apollo 11

Alarms, loss of communication and system failures plagued the first mission to land on the Moon

03:04:15:47
"Apollo 11, Apollo 11, this is Houston. Do you read? Over."
Bruce McCandless, CAPCOM

03:04:15:59
"Apollo 11, Apollo 11, this is Houston. Do you read? Over."
Bruce McCandless, CAPCOM

03:04:17:00
"Apollo 11, Apollo 11, this is Houston. We are reading you weakly. Go ahead. Over."
Bruce McCandless, CAPCOM

03:04:19:32
"Apollo 11, this is Houston. Are you in the process of acquiring data on the burn? Over."
Bruce McCandless, CAPCOM

03:04:21:37
"Apollo 11, Apollo 11, this is Houston. How do you read?"
Bruce McCandless, CAPCOM

03:04:16:11
"..."
Unidentified crew member, Apollo 11

03:04:16:59
"Houston, Apollo 11. Over."
Unidentified crew member, Apollo 11

03:04:21:43
"Reading you loud and clear, Houston. How's us?"
Neil Armstrong, Apollo 11 commander

© All photos NASA

Apollo 11's journey to the Moon

It was one small step for a man, one giant leap for mankind

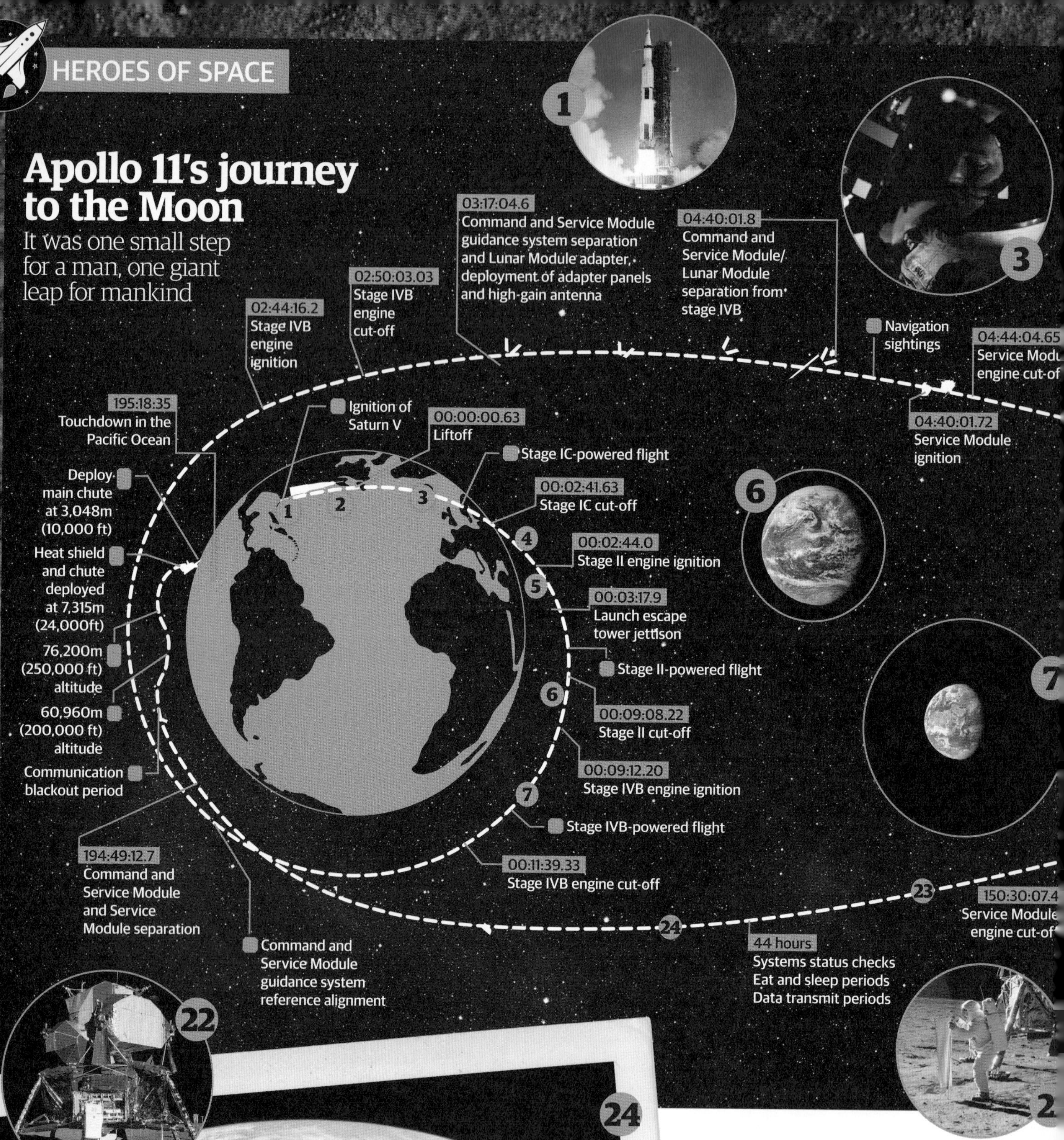

03:17:04.6
Command and Service Module guidance system separation and Lunar Module adapter, deployment of adapter panels and high-gain antenna

04:40:01.8
Command and Service Module/ Lunar Module separation from stage IVB

02:50:03.03
Stage IVB engine cut-off

02:44:16.2
Stage IVB engine ignition

Navigation sightings

04:44:04.65
Service Modu engine cut-of

195:18:35
Touchdown in the Pacific Ocean

Ignition of Saturn V

00:00:00.63
Liftoff

Stage IC-powered flight

04:40:01.72
Service Module ignition

Deploy main chute at 3,048m (10,000 ft)

00:02:41.63
Stage IC cut-off

Heat shield and chute deployed at 7,315m (24,000ft)

00:02:44.0
Stage II engine ignition

76,200m (250,000 ft) altitude

00:03:17.9
Launch escape tower jettison

60,960m (200,000 ft) altitude

Stage II-powered flight

Communication blackout period

00:09:08.22
Stage II cut-off

00:09:12.20
Stage IVB engine ignition

194:49:12.7
Command and Service Module and Service Module separation

Stage IVB-powered flight

Command and Service Module guidance system reference alignment

00:11:39.33
Stage IVB engine cut-off

150:30:07.4
Service Module engine cut-of

44 hours
Systems status checks
Eat and sleep periods
Data transmit periods

instead it gave us the code number of the alarm," said Aldrin. "It was disturbing and distracting and we didn't know what it meant."

The 1201 and 1202 alarms were obscure codes – and in effect the same error – that flashed up as Armstrong manually attempted to bring the Lunar Module down. Nobody seemed to know what the codes meant, except for two men: Jack Garman, a NASA computer engineer who had come across the codes before during a practice run, and Steve Bales, who was the Apollo guidance officer. The alarms were being caused by a problem with the landing radar that was stealing precious computing cycles, and the throttle control algorithm was barely working. The computer's 72kb of memory, barely enough to write a sentence in a modern word processor, was struggling as commands into

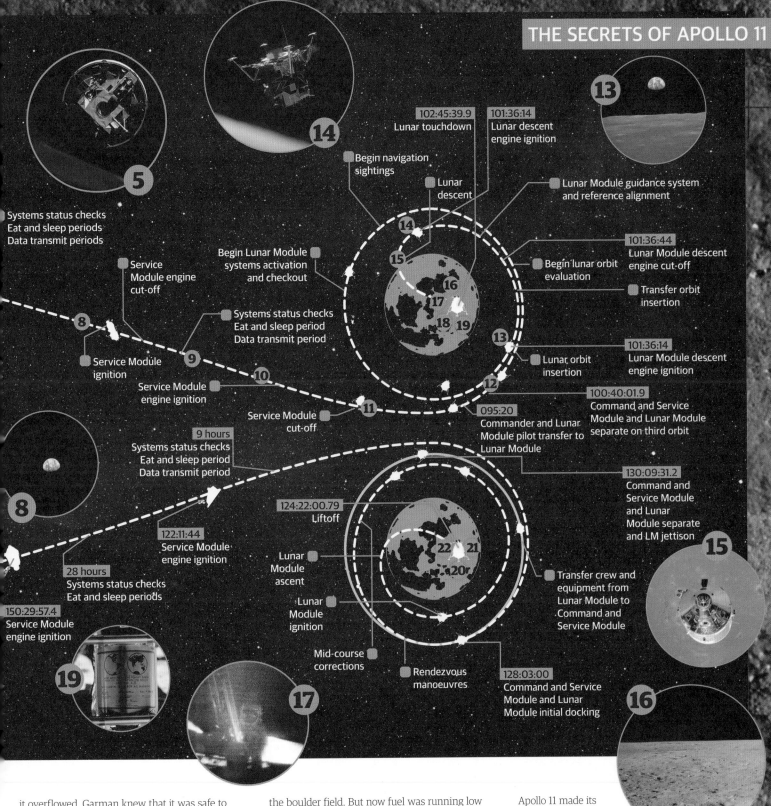

5

14

13

102:45:39.9
Lunar touchdown

101:36:14
Lunar descent
engine ignition

Begin navigation
sightings

Lunar
descent

Lunar Module guidance system
and reference alignment

14

Systems status checks
Eat and sleep periods
Data transmit periods

Service
Module engine
cut-off

Begin Lunar Module
systems activation
and checkout

15

16

17

18 **19**

Begin lunar orbit
evaluation

101:36:44
Lunar Module descent
engine cut-off

Transfer orbit
insertion

Systems status checks
Eat and sleep period
Data transmit period

8

Service Module
ignition

9

Service Module
engine ignition

10

Service Module
cut-off

11

13

12

Lunar orbit
insertion

101:36:14
Lunar Module descent
engine ignition

100:40:01.9
Command and Service
Module and Lunar Module
separate on third orbit

095:20
Commander and Lunar
Module pilot transfer to
Lunar Module

130:09:31.2
Command and
Service Module
and Lunar
Module separate
and LM jettison

9 hours
Systems status checks
Eat and sleep period
Data transmit period

8

122:11:44
Service Module
engine ignition

28 hours
Systems status checks
Eat and sleep periods

150:29:57.4
Service Module
engine ignition

19

17

124:22:00.79
Liftoff

Lunar
Module
ascent

Lunar
Module
ignition

Mid-course
corrections

Rendezvous
manoeuvres

22 **21**

20

Transfer crew and
equipment from
Lunar Module to
Command and
Service Module

15

128:03:00
Command and Service
Module and Lunar
Module initial docking

16

it overflowed. Garman knew that it was safe to
continue and allow the computer to handle matters.
Its priority scheduling routines, which have formed
some of the bases of a lot of modern code, were
dumping lower priority tasks in favour of the ones
critical to the lunar landing.

As the Eagle approached the surface on
automatic, Armstrong and Aldrin realised that
the scenery outside of the window didn't look
familiar to them. "I think we may be a little long,"
commented Armstrong, referring to the Eagle
having overshot its planned landing site. Looming
ahead of them was a dangerous-looking boulder
field, and coming down on any of those giant rocks
the size of houses would have damaged or perhaps
even destroyed the Eagle. Armstrong took manual
control, using the thrusters to take the Eagle over

the boulder field. But now fuel was running low
and there was no turning back. Armstrong had to
land the Eagle - somewhere, within minutes - or
they would be out of fuel and crash. "We'd never
been this close in training," said Kranz. "We started
a stopwatch running, with a controller calling off
seconds of fuel remaining."

If things were tense in mission control, on board
the Eagle Armstrong and Aldrin had everything
under control. With only 13 seconds of fuel left

Apollo 11 made its
safe landing in the Sea
of Tranquillity. History
had been made. "Houston,
Tranquillity Base here," Armstrong
radioed home. "The Eagle has landed."

In private, Aldrin took out a small cup, some
wine and bread and said Holy Communion. The
wine, under one-sixth Earth gravity, apparently
curled up in the cup. After reading a section of the

*"We felt that our survival was in the
probability of 99 per cent. There were a lot
of risks involved"* Buzz Aldrin

Your memories

> "Apollo 11 is one of my first memories. I got to stay up late a few nights which was the big thrill at the time. I remember the fuzzy pictures on our black-and-white TV. It made me a life-long fan of space exploration."
> James McGarry, @jmcgarry0

> "I witnessed the launch on TV. The feeling I had was the whole world was watching with anticipation, pride and the reality... We are actually going to the Moon!"
> Daniel Porter, @danielporter731

> "Watched it all with a friend on a grainy TV up in their loft where the best signal [in the house] was. We were so aware of how absolutely extraordinary this was – and not so secretly hoping aliens would make an appearance!"
> Suzanne Conboy-Hill, @strayficshion

> "I was seven and just about remember it being on TV. I remember the landing and 'Live from the Moon' on screen. It was magical."
> John Davies, @JohnnyD_cm

Left: The iconic photo of Aldrin standing on the surface, with Armstrong and the Lunar Module reflected in his visor

Bottom left: The flight controllers erupt into applause as Apollo 11 splashes down in the Pacific Ocean on 24 July 1969, successfully completing the mission

Bottom right: Aldrin smiles inside the Lunar Module

Gospel of St John, Aldrin said a few words, with Armstrong respectfully looking on. NASA had been threatened with legal action by Madalyn Murray O'Hair, an atheist, after the crew of Apollo 8 had read from the book of Genesis, so Aldrin's heartfelt ceremony never made it to the airwaves.

The original plan had been for the crew to get some sleep, but with that much adrenaline pumping through their veins that was never going to happen. At 02:39 UTC on the morning of 21 July, Armstrong made his way through the hatch and down the ladder before stepping foot on the surface of the Moon for the first time and saying those immortal words: "That's one small step for [a] man, one giant leap for mankind."

After exiting the Lunar Module, Armstrong and Aldrin only had a few hours to not only collect precious rock samples, but also deploy a series of experiments on the lunar surface. Solar wind experiments, a laser retro-reflector that is still used to this day to measure the Earth-Moon distance, seismometers and more were all deployed. Armstrong is cited as saying he felt like a five year old in a candy store, with not enough time to do all the things he wanted to. Standing on the Moon must have been an incredible experience. Aldrin described the scene around him as one of "magnificent desolation", adding that "you could look at the horizon and see very clearly because there was no atmosphere, there was no haze or anything".

As Armstrong walked around setting up instruments and picking up rocks, Aldrin hopped around on the surface, testing what the best way to move about in the low gravity was. Most of the pictures taken during the landing are of Aldrin on the surface; barely half a dozen show Armstrong, and none clearly. That's because Armstrong had the camera for most of the Moon walk. While on the surface, the crew also had terrific problems with the American flag. It had a telescoping boom arm to hold it out in lieu of any wind to hold it up. The two astronauts wrestled to get the boom arm to extend fully, but it would not, so the flag had a small kink in it. They also found that it was almost impossible to get the flagpole to go deep enough into the ground and, in the end, they only just managed to get it to stay upright. Both of the crew worried it would fall over live on TV, and probably as President Nixon was on the phone to them. But it remained upright during the broadcasts and telephone calls.

After collecting their rocks and clambering back into the Lunar Module, the crew took off their boots and backpacks, and began to throw anything not of vital importance back onto the lunar surface. This included urine bags, empty food packs, empty cameras and so on. But to the crew, they were just getting in the way and not needed. There was time for one final crisis. The interior of the Lunar Module was cramped and, moving around in their bulky spacesuits, one of the astronauts had knocked out the switch for the circuit breaker that fired the ascent rocket that would take them home.

This was a real bottleneck moment for the mission. "If for some reason the ascent engine didn't work, there was no way to rescue the crew," said

Michael Collins' forgotten photograph

The Apollo 11 Command Module pilot reveals an old photo he believes NASA never used

Michael Collins

Buzz Aldrin,
Lunar Module pilot

Neil Armstrong,
commander

Michael Collins,
Command Module pilot

"Rather than worry, we'd face them when the time came and we'd work as hard as we could to fix the problem" Buzz Aldrin

Kranz. Armstrong and Aldrin would be stranded on the Moon. The concern was so serious that President Nixon had a speech prepared, while mission control would close down communications with Armstrong and Aldrin after a clergyman had "condemned their souls to the deepest of the deep". Without that circuit breaker the crew were facing that lonely fate, but their training would not have allowed them to give up. "Rather than worry about things like that, we'd face them when the time came and we'd work as hard as we could to fix the problem until our oxygen ran out," said Aldrin.

In the end, the solution was remarkably simple. Jabbing the end of a pen into the slot where the broken switch had been, Aldrin was able to push the circuit breaker in. The ascent rocket fired and the two Moonwalkers were on their way home, via a rendezvous with Michael Collins in the Command Module. As the Eagle took off, the flag finally did blow over, and to this day it lays flattened, bleached out by solar radiation.

"Neil could be very closed off emotionally"

James Hansen is the only author to write an official biography on space hero Neil Armstrong

"In some ways Neil was a very simple and very straightforward type of person, but at the same time very complex. That sounds like a contradiction, but the human personality is an amazing and difficult thing.

Neil could be very closed off emotionally in many respects, and very private and unwilling to share his inner thoughts. But at the same time – in certain social settings when he was comfortable, certainly around his fellow pilots and astronauts – he could be very friendly, had a great sense of humour and was just a great person to be around. I was interested in getting under his skin in a way. In writing the book, I didn't really want to turn it into a psychobiography where I try to apply psychology concepts to his personality. At the same time, I did want to understand what made him tick.

I'm a strong believer that the child is the father to the man. You have to really understand what goes on in childhood development, for example his parents, siblings, family and community, to really understand why a person becomes what they become."

Houston, we've had a problem

Planned as NASA's third lunar landing, Apollo 13 gripped the world's attention for all the wrong reasons, as a flight to the Moon turned into a battle for survival

O n 11 April 1970, as Apollo 13 blasted clear of Cape Canaveral right on schedule, none of those on board could have foreseen the struggle for survival they were soon to encounter. The crew included two freshman astronauts - Command Module pilot Jack Swigert and Lunar Module pilot Fred Haise, but was led by one of NASA's most experienced spacefarers, Gemini and Apollo 8 veteran Jim Lovell (Lovell and Haise had been backup crew for the Apollo 11 mission, while Swigert was a late replacement for Ken Mattingly, who had been grounded as an infection risk after one of his children contracted the rubella virus).

The first two days of their cruise towards the Moon were routine, but 56 hours into the flight, a routine request to stir the service module's fuel tanks rapidly spiralled into a crisis. As Swigert triggered the stirring motor, a loud bang echoed through the craft and warning lights flashed to indicate that one of the module's power circuits was rapidly draining. Swigert and Lovell reported back to mission control with typical understatement: "Okay Houston, we've had a problem here."

Now the spacecraft began shaking from side to side, and as Lovell struggled to stabilise it, he spotted a jet of gas escaping into space. On-board gauges and telemetry signals received at Houston showed one of the service module's two oxygen tanks as empty, and two of the three batteries designed to power the command and service modules (CSM) throughout the mission were now flat. Even worse, pressure in the second oxygen tank was falling.

Now, the problem became clear - the spacecraft oxygen tanks provided not just fuel and air, but were also linked to a fuel cell that charged the batteries. An explosion (later traced to poorly insulated wiring) had ruptured the system, but the tanks were still pumping oxygen to it.

With Apollo 13 some 330,000 km (205,000 miles) from Earth and still Moon-bound, the crew and staff at mission control, led by flight director Gene Kranz, had to think fast. After shutting down the fuel cell to preserve the remaining oxygen, their first thought was to draw power from the independent systems on the Lunar Module (LM) Aquarius, but this idea was soon abandoned, as the demands on the LM's limited batteries would be too high. Instead, the crew were ordered to use Aquarius as a 'lifeboat', transferring supplies into the cramped vehicle (only intended for two astronauts), before shutting down the CSM systems completely to preserve them for return to Earth, and locking themselves in.

Within three hours, the immediate crisis was over, but the struggle to get the crew safely back to Earth was just beginning. NASA's contingency plans to abort a mission in this phase called for jettisoning the LM and also required a fully fuelled CSM, so were obviously out of the question. Instead, Kranz and his team realised the only option was to swing the entire spacecraft around the far side of the Moon, using the LM's small engines to enter a return trajectory. The timing of these engine burns would be critical - 30.7 seconds was needed on lunar approach to put the spacecraft into a 'free return' trajectory (where the Moon's gravity would effectively swing the spacecraft around and hurl it back towards Earth), and then a longer burn during return would speed up re-entry by ten hours (so that splashdown would occur in the Pacific rather than the Indian Ocean). As the crippled spacecraft swung around the far side of the Moon on 15 April, and communications with Earth were temporarily cut off, its crew set an unwanted new record as the furthest humans from Earth, some 400,171 km (248,655 miles) away.

Sealed into the cramped Lunar Module, survival for the crew now became the overriding priority; all four ground-control shifts at Houston were drafted in to look at various aspects of the problem. Oxygen supplies were sufficient even with three men on board, but water was limited, and power consumption had to be reduced, so television transmissions were abandoned and even radio communications scaled back. A critical danger, however, was the buildup of toxic carbon dioxide - both elements of the spacecraft used canisters loaded with a chemical called lithium hydroxide to 'scrub' the excess CO_2 from the air, but the LM's supply was being rapidly used up, and even though the astronauts had brought over extra canisters from the CSM, they were not compatible. Working with a list of available materials on the LM, engineers at Houston came up with instructions for the crew to make an improvised adapter, nicknamed the 'mailbox', using a spacesuit connecting hose.

As the spacecraft neared Earth, a final set of challenges awaited. Most critical was the need to power up the CSM from its shutdown state without causing further damage. No one had thought that such a procedure would ever have to be done in space, and the grounded Mattingly, along with flight controller John Aaron and others, worked feverishly to develop a safe procedure.

On 17 April, with millions around the world listening in to commentary on their every move, the astronauts re-entered the command module Odyssey and brought it back to life. After abandoning the damaged service module, one last risky procedure involved separating from the trusty Aquarius and pushing it away by forcing air into the connecting tunnel between the two modules.

Having avoided the risks of a collision during re-entry, the cone-shaped command module plunged back into the atmosphere. With no way of knowing whether the explosion had damaged the heat shields or descent parachute system, Houston and the world held their breath - and tension worsened as the usual radio blackout on re-entry lengthened from an expected four and a half minutes to six. There was silence as the world feared the worst. Finally, to everyone's relief, Swigert's voice emerged over the crackling radio. Nine minutes later, Odyssey splashed down, within 6.5 km (4 miles) of the recovery ship USS Iwo Jima, and the celebrations could begin.

APOLLO XIII

EX LUNA, SCIENTIA

Apollo 13 flight directors celebrate the successful splashdown of the Odyssey after the damaged craft's harrowing flight

Swigert aboard Apollo 13 on its return journey to Earth, with some of the improvised hoses used to filter the astronauts' air supply

CARL SAGAN
The visionary

We reveal how the futuristic and theoretical visions of the influential scientist Carl Sagan became reality

Written by Ian Evenden

© Kenneth C. Zirkel Carl Sagan speaks at Cornell University in 1987

"As a boy Kepler had been captured by a vision of cosmic splendour, a harmony of the worlds which he sought so tirelessly all his life"
Cosmos: A Personal Voyage

Sagan's admiration of Johannes Kepler, the 16th to 17th century German astronomer who formulated laws of planetary motion and provided some of the work Newton's theory of universal gravitation would be built upon, is shared by many at NASA, it seems. Sagan was particularly prophetic here, speaking of Kepler seeking worlds his entire life, as it was the Kepler space telescope, named after the astronomer, that would have this as its mission.

The spacecraft, now retired, was launched in 2009 with a mission to survey a small portion of the Milky Way for Earth-sized exoplanets in or near the habitable zone around their host stars. Not only did Kepler discover 2,662 exoplanets, having surveyed over half a million stars, but it kept working for 9.6 years, far in excess of its initial 3.5-year life expectancy. Even when its reaction wheels had failed, robbing it of the accuracy to collect exoplanet data, Kepler kept on working, its new mission to search a larger area of the galaxy for supernovae, as well as looking within the Solar System for asteroids and comets.

Above: The Kepler mission blasts off on 7 March 2009

Left: The Arecibo message, sent from Puerto Rico in 1974

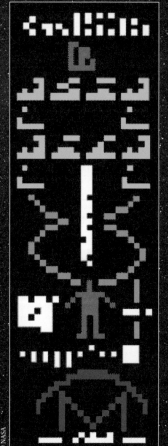
© NASA

"It is easy to create an interstellar radio message which can be recognised as emanating unambiguously from intelligent beings"
Smithsonian magazine, May 1978

Just four years before Sagan's claim, a message was sent from the Arecibo Observatory in Puerto Rico in the direction of the globular star cluster M13. It consisted of the numbers one to ten; information about the Earth, humans and our Solar System plus the atomic numbers of the elements that make up DNA. Designed to be easily read and interpreted, it will still take 25,000 years for it to reach the cluster, with another 25,000 for any reply from intelligent life to be received. M13 was chosen because it was in the right place in the sky at the time the observatory was reopening after remodelling work. Since then, however, further messages have been sent to Sun-like stars with exoplanets, including two - in 2008 and 2009 - to the Gliese 581 system just 20 light years away and containing what at the time were the most Earth-like exoplanets known.

"Astronomically, the USSR and the United States are the same place" *Cosmos*

Sagan is writing about the Cold War here. He had a lot to say on the matter of nuclear weapons, describing the US/Soviet face-off as two enemies in a room awash with gasoline, the one with 9,000 matches worrying that the one with 7,000 was getting ahead. As a broader statement on human conflict, however, it's absolutely timeless.

No matter how deeply we are divided, we all live together on a tiny speck of dust. By showing that if you have a distant enough viewpoint, both sides in the conflict appear the same, he's commenting on the futility of war, something he described as "murder writ large", and the need for us to come together as a species in harmony with our planet.

The Earth and Moon from Saturn as seen by Cassini

© NASA

"The cosmos is all that is or ever was or ever will be"
Cosmos

Assuming Sagan is using 'cosmos' here to mean the universe, he might not be entirely correct. If we are trapped within our universe and are unable to even see out of it, then this may well be seen as correct. However, we are able to hypothesise situations in which there could be more than one cosmos. The many-worlds interpretation of quantum mechanics, for example, had been around for 23 years when Sagan wrote those words in his book's introduction. Since then we've seen research into the shape of the universe, into whether it really is infinite or a bubble nestled alongside others. Stephen Hawking's final paper, published in 2018, aimed to test a theory that proposes parallel universes, and predicts a period before the Big Bang when time was like 'a sphere without edges' instead of the directional arrow we're used to. In string theory - an attempt to merge quantum mechanics and general relativity - we could be part of a ten-dimensional multiverse with infinite universes governed by different physical laws. Include string theory offshoot M-theory - Hawking's favourite candidate for a complete theory of the universe - and the number of dimensions rises to 11. Of course, if Sagan used 'cosmos' to mean 'multiverse', then he's completely right.

"We don't yet know whether the universe is open or closed. More than that, there are a few astronomers who doubt that the redshift of distant galaxies is due to the Doppler effect, who are sceptical of the expanding universe and the Big Bang"
Cosmos: A Personal Voyage

The shape of the universe - whether it's flat and infinite, curves in a way that means its edges must somehow meet or curves into dimensions we cannot appreciate - also tells us about its eventual fate, and has been the subject of much debate and experiment. If the shape is closed gravity will eventually stop its expansion, and it will contract back to a singularity. Unless, that is, dark energy overpowers gravity and it keeps expanding forever.

If the shape is open, dark energy will overpower gravity and it will expand forever, perhaps even overcoming the binding forces between individual particles. If the shape is flat - and this is currently best supported by experimental and observational evidence - then expansion continues forever, but its rate decelerates until dark energy once again takes over and it tears itself apart. As for those who doubt the Big Bang and the expansion of the universe, there's probably a reason these ideas are filed under 'non-standard cosmology'. However, with new experimental and observational data, who knows what can become 'standard'?

Sagan poses with a model of the Viking lander in Death Valley, California, as part of his *Cosmos* series

Illustration of a high-redshift Milky Way-like galaxy in the early universe with a background quasar shinning through a 'super halo' of hydrogen gas

© Alexandra Angelich (NRAO/AUI/NSF)

Carl Sagan, Bruce Murray and Louis Friedman, the founders of the Planetary Society, at the time of signing the papers formally incorporating the organisation. The fourth person is Harry Ashmore, an advisor who greatly helped in the founding of the Society

"Those who are sceptical about carbon dioxide greenhouse warming might profitably note the massive greenhouse effect on Venus"

Pale Blue Dot: A Vision of the Human Future in Space

A quote that seems extremely pertinent today, Sagan goes on to deride those who claim that the greenhouse effect on Earth is somehow a 'hoax'. NASA's Earth-observing satellites have been publishing their results since 1999 as the NASA Earth Observatory. Recently they have recorded the second-lowest level of Arctic sea ice, Cyclone Hikka hitting Oman, dust storms in southern Africa, unusually heavy snow in Montana and Canada and the remains of Hurricane Lorenzo approaching Ireland after travelling further north and east across the Atlantic than any previous storm of the same strength. NASA's Earth Observing System, made up of satellites launched from 1966 onwards, provides much of the data. Only ten satellites, the oldest having launched in 1999, still have active missions, but further missions, including some based on the ISS, are planned. The European Space Agency also launches Earth-observing satellites, with the Far-infrared Outgoing Radiation Understanding and Monitoring (FORUM) mission to measure the radiation emitted by Earth into space selected in September for a launch in 2026.

"The cosmos is also within us. We're made of star-stuff. We are a way for the cosmos to know itself"

Cosmos: A Personal Voyage

What Sagan is getting at here is stellar or supernova nucleosynthesis, the creation of heavy elements, many of which end up inside our bodies, during the lives and death explosions of gigantic stars. The Big Bang produced hydrogen, helium and lithium, plus a few heavier isotopes that decayed back into helium and lithium.

This was enough to produce stars, which fuse hydrogen into more helium, and as the stars heat up heavier elements are produced, including the carbon and oxygen essential for life on Earth. This chain keeps going until it reaches iron, the first element that requires more energy to fuse than the process produces. Anything heavier than iron must be produced in an environment with greater heat and pressure than the interior of a star, and an exploding massive star is just such a place. Everything around us and within us, apart from hydrogen, helium and lithium, was produced in the fusion furnaces within stars, meaning we are inseparable from the universe around us.

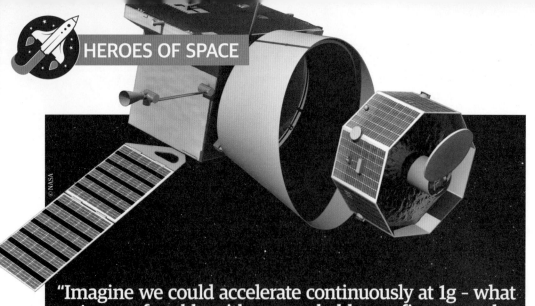

"Advances in medicine and agriculture have saved vastly more lives than have been lost in all the wars in history"

The Demon-Haunted World: Science as a Candle in the Dark

Advances in medicine continue to this day, though perhaps nothing with the wide-ranging effects of the discovery of antibiotics or antiseptics. Take the mosquito: this tiny flying bloodsucker was responsible for the deaths of a million people in 2018 alone, according to the American Mosquito Control Association, and could have killed over 50 billion humans over the last 100,000 years. The culprit isn't the mosquito at all, but parasites and viruses they carry in their digestive system. The best known, Malaria, is a parasite with a life cycle that takes it from mosquito to human and back again. Modern medicine is fighting back, however, with a vaccine undergoing pilot trials in Malawi, Ghana and Kenya.

"Imagine we could accelerate continuously at 1g – what we're comfortable with on good old terra firma – to the midpoint of our voyage, and decelerate continuously at 1g until we arrive at our destination. It would take a day to get to Mars, a week-and-a-half to Pluto, a year to the Oort Cloud and a few years to the nearest stars"

Pale Blue Dot: A Vision of the Human Future in Space

Alternatives to the solid- and liquid-fuelled booster rockets and gas thrusters we rely on to propel our spacecraft once in space are being actively sought. Solar sails, which harness the energy of the Sun for movement, have been tested, with the Japanese IKAROS probe heading to Venus in 2010, and the Breakthrough Starshot project is planning a fleet of tiny probes sent to Proxima Centauri by lightsail, pushed by Earth-based lasers for an initial acceleration burst of 10,000g. Slowing down at the destination would be difficult, however. The lack of friction in space means once you've accelerated to a speed you stick to it, hence Sagan's careful wording of

acceleration and deceleration. Other ideas have included the crazy-sounding 1958 Orion project that propelled spacecraft by exploding nuclear bombs behind them and riding the shockwave.

Ion thrusters - possibly powered by a nuclear reactor - that shoot charged particles out like a rocket have been tested on the Deep Space 1, Dawn and BepiColombo missions, among others. Sagan's dream of a smooth 1g acceleration and deceleration, however, is still some distance away.

Above: The ESA's BepiColombo mission will use solar-powered ion thrusters as part of its flybys of Venus and Mercury between 2020 and 2025

The Anopheles stephensi mosquito is a known malarial vector with a distribution that ranges from Egypt all the way to China

"I stress that the universe is made mostly of nothing, that something is the exception"

The Varieties of Scientific Experience: A Personal View of the Search for God

The distribution of matter in the universe is clearer to us today than it was when Sagan was writing. Not only are the distances between clumps of matter - galaxies - absolutely huge, but 95 per cent of the universe is comprised of something we can't detect in any way. Dark matter, which makes up 27 per cent of the total mass-energy of the universe, can at least be observed through its gravitational effects. Dark energy - 68 per cent of the mass-energy of the universe - is even more mysterious, existing only as the most well-accepted hypothesis to explain observations that the universe is expanding at an accelerating rate. These percentages come in part from Planck Space Telescope data released in 2013, so Sagan couldn't have known of them, but dark matter can trace its roots back to the 1920s and 1930s, when astronomers such as Jan Oort and Fritz Zwicky were studying local stars and galactic clusters respectively. Dark energy has its origins in Einstein's calculations for general relativity, proposed as a way to balance out gravity to keep the universe static. This is one of the most hotly contested areas of astronomical research, and promises great revelations.

This happy image from the Hubble Space Telescope shows the view of distant galaxies being gravitationally lensed by a large mass in between. Predicted by Einstein, images such as this are evidence for mass we cannot see

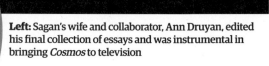

Left: Sagan's wife and collaborator, Ann Druyan, edited his final collection of essays and was instrumental in bringing *Cosmos* to television

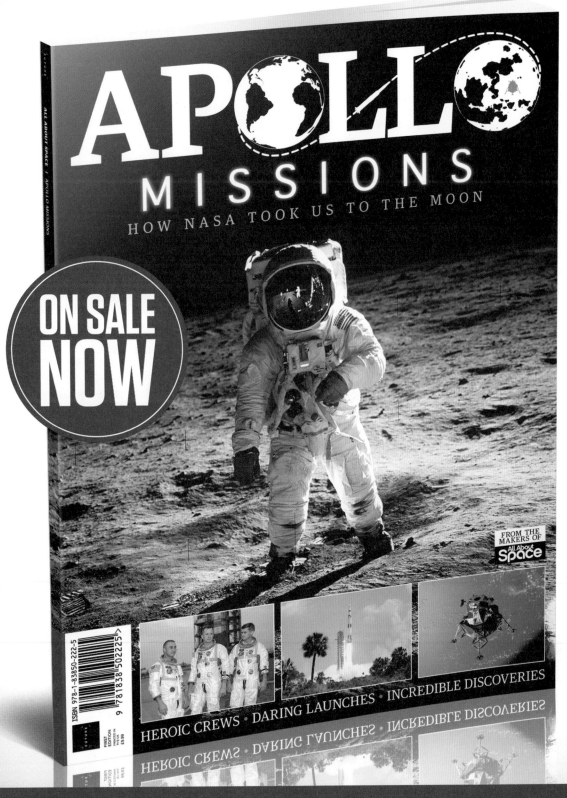

What we learned from the Challenger disaster

© NASA·Getty

The first loss of a Space Shuttle and its crew was a preventable disaster, but it would go onto largely change NASA for the better

Reported by Ian Evenden

Just 73 seconds was all it took from the launch of Space Shuttle mission STS-51-L on 28 January 1986 to the Shuttle's disintegration over the Atlantic and the loss of all seven of its crew. It was a routine mission to deploy a data relay satellite and test a probe designed to observe Halley's Comet, but was notable for the presence of Christa McAuliffe - the first teacher in space, and a civilian, in the crew. She had been chosen for the mission out of an initial application pool of more than 11,000, and was planning to carry out experiments and beam back lessons to Earth in order to rekindle interest in the US space program, remind Americans of the role teachers play in society and demonstrate the reliability of spaceflight.

Challenger was completely destroyed in the disaster, which was traced to the failure of an O-ring seal in the Shuttle's right-hand solid rocket booster. This allowed hot gases to flare out, burning through the strut attaching the booster to the external fuel tank and causing the two to clash together, eventually leading to structural failure of the fuel tank and allowing all parts of the launch vehicle to fly apart, disintegrating under the pressure of aerodynamic forces.

It's not a long time, but it's possible for a great deal to happen in such a compressed period. Those 73 seconds led to an investigation that took months to complete its analysis, and a total shutdown of the Shuttle program for 32 months. The morning of 28 January had been cold, and ice had formed on the launch pad at Kennedy Space Center, Florida. Challenger's launch was delayed by two hours to allow the ice to melt, but this wasn't the first delay to the mission. Originally scheduled for July 1985, STS-51-L was to be the 25th Shuttle mission, and the tenth flight of Challenger. Delays put the launch back to November. A Columbia mission scheduled to go up just before Challenger was also delayed, pushing the mission back even further to 22 January 1986, then 25 January. Bad weather set in, and the launch was rescheduled for

27 January, then finally 28 January after a problem with a hatch handle.

Engineers were worried that the amount of ice present on the pad could damage the Shuttle at liftoff, perhaps striking the Shuttle's thermal protection tiles. The temperature on the morning of launch was as low as -2.2 degrees Celsius (28 degrees Fahrenheit) - the minimum required for a launch was -1 degrees Celsius (30.2 degrees Fahrenheit), and the previous coldest launch had been at 12 degrees Celsius (53.6 degrees Fahrenheit). But despite managers at the launch pad voicing their concerns, the mission manager in Houston, Texas, gave clearance to launch after a final inspection showed the ice to be melting.

The Shuttle wasn't certified to operate in temperatures that low, and concerns had already been raised about the O-rings. The solid rocket boosters were constructed in sections, which were joined together at the Kennedy Space Center prior to launch. Each joint was sealed with two rubber rings to prevent the hot gas from the burning propellant going the wrong way up the booster, instead being forced out the nozzle at the bottom. A 1971 report had discussed a possible booster failure caused by hot gas burning through "adjacent to [liquid hydrogen/oxygen] tank or orbiter," and warning that "timely sensing may not be feasible and abort not possible". It wasn't unknown for the O-ring seals to bend, opening a hole through which hot gas could escape, eroding the surface of the ring thanks to the drop in pressure - a 1977 test managed to do it using just

The casualties

Francis Richard Scobee
Commander

Michael John Smith
Pilot

Ellison Shoji Onizuka
Mission specialist

Judith Arlene Resnik
Mission specialist

Ronald Erwin McNair
Mission specialist

Gregory Bruce Jarvis
Payload specialist

Sharon Christa McAuliffe
Teacher and payload specialist

All headshots © NASA

Minute by minute

What happened during the Challenger disaster?

The disaster was over quickly, but a lot happened in those 73 fatal seconds

1 BLASTOFF

T=0.00s

As the command to ignite the solid fuel rockets is sent, mission specialist Judith Resnik can be heard to say, "All Right!"

2 BLACK SMOKE

T+0.678s

Smoke from just above the O-ring in Challenger's right-hand booster is captured on film, but not seen until it is developed.

3 THROTTLE UP

T+4.364s

The main engine throttle is increased from 90 per cent to 104 per cent, as planned.

4 THROTTLE BACK

T+19.885

Commands are sent to the main engines to throttle down to 94 per cent.

5 HIGH AND FAST

T+28.000

The Shuttle reaches 3,050 metres (10,000 feet) in altitude and half the speed of sound.

6 SUPERSONIC

T+40.000

At almost 6,100 metres (20,000 feet), Challenger breaks the sound barrier. Engines throttle down to 65 per cent.

7 FLASHES

T+45.217

A flash is observed behind the Shuttle's right wing, followed by two more three seconds after the first.

O-ring failure

The O-ring seals – not designed to handle cold conditions – failed and allowed hot, pressurised gas to burn through the skin of the booster, severing its connection to the external fuel tank and leading to structural failure.

8 FLAMES SEEN

T+59.753

Flames can be seen on the side of the right-hand booster. A plume of exhaust can also be seen by tracking cameras on the booster.

9 O-RING FAILURE

T+72.284

The right-hand booster pulls away from the strut that connects its base to the external fuel tank. A large ball of fire appears.

10 FINAL TRANSMISSION

T+73.000

Over the intercom, pilot Michael J. Smith says, "Uh-oh".

11 FIREBALL

T+73.191

Cameras record a brilliant flash as Challenger is engulfed in yellow and red flames.

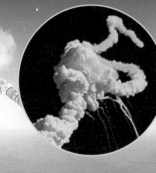

12 BREAK UP

T+74.587

Another flash as, travelling at twice the speed of sound, Challenger disintegrates in flight. The last of the propellant in the external tank ignites, leaving the two solid rocket boosters to continue climbing.

13 RIGHT BOOSTER DETONATED

T+110.250

Safety officers signal the self-destruct packages in the boosters to detonate.

14 CABIN DOWN

T+3 min 58 sec

The crew cabin hits the Atlantic Ocean, subjecting the crew to a force of 200G. It disintegrates and debris sinks to the bottom.

15 DEBRIS

T+5 min 36 sec

The final large piece, thought to be one of Challenger's wings, splashes into the ocean. Small pieces of debris continue to fall for some time.

pressurised water - but despite the concerns of engineers, including a letter to the manager of the Solid Rocket Booster project, the boosters were approved for flight in 1980.

STS-2, the second Shuttle mission, showed serious erosion of the O-rings. The seals were redesignated as a Criticality 1 part, meaning their failure could result in the destruction of the orbiter, but the design wasn't changed. Damage to O-rings on subsequent flights was labelled an 'acceptable risk', even when seven of the nine Shuttle flights in 1985 showed such damage. It was a previous Challenger mission, STS-51-B in April 1985, that finally saw the design change process begin, because the primary O-ring on the left-hand booster was damaged so severely that for the first time the secondary ring was damaged too.

Additional steel was added around the seal, but the redesigned steel cases were still in production at the time of the Challenger disaster. "Today," wrote a *New York Times* report at the time, "they are the basis for the creation of improved boosters. [But] did officials who knew about these casings press to continue flights? Why was the new design being applied slowly?"

These are, of course, excellent questions, but the Rogers Commission, set up by President Reagan to investigate the disaster, steered away from them, its chairman William P. Rogers stating that the panel should deal only with events leading directly to the disaster. The commission - which included the first man on the Moon Neil Armstrong;

"Despite the concerns of engineers, the boosters were approved for flight in 1980"

physicist Richard Feynman, who'd worked on the Manhattan Project; astronaut Sally Ride, who'd flown twice on Challenger and the first man to break the sound barrier, Chuck Yeager, among other Air Force personnel, aeronautics experts, scientists and engineers - would, however, be strongly critical.

The commission found that NASA had known about the problem with the O-rings - and their

Above: A joint that retained traces of O-ring seal tracks. Samples of the track material underwent chemical analysis that indicated that they were not composed of degraded O-ring seal material

Left: Challenger sits atop the crawler-transporter on its way to the launch pad

potential for calamity - as early as 1977. Both NASA and its contractor, Morton-Thiokol, had failed to respond adequately to the design flaw. The commission described the disaster as "an accident rooted in history," criticising the decision-making process that had led to the launch of the Shuttle that icy morning. It was "based on incomplete and sometimes misleading information," the report states, and that "NASA management structure ... permitted internal flight-safety problems to bypass key Shuttle managers."

Richard Feynman was an outspoken member of the commission, investigating in his own style and annoying Rogers to the extent that he called the physicist "a real pain". In a televised hearing, Feynman produced some of the O-ring material and dunked it in iced water, demonstrating for the cameras how it became rigid and more prone to failure when it was chilled. "I discovered that when you put some pressure on it for a while and then undo it, it does not stretch back," he said. "There is no resilience in this particular material when it is at a temperature of 32 degrees Fahrenheit [0 degrees Celsius]."

When not utilising props to devastating effect, his interviews with NASA officials demonstrated that basic safety terminology was being misunderstood, and that the probabilities of failure generated by the agency were far from accurate. Taking the example of NASA's claimed 1 in 100,000 chance of a catastrophic failure of a Shuttle, he realised this meant they could be launched for 274 years and expect only one incident. NASA had used these inaccurate figures to persuade McAuliffe to join the mission, and Feynman felt that the recruitment of civilians required honesty about the risks of spaceflight.

A 2013 film, *The Challenger*, revealed astronaut Sally Ride had secretly provided a commission member, General Donald Kutyna, with NASA test results showing the effect of cold on the O-rings. Kutyna was then able to point Feynman in the right direction, asking him an apparently innocuous question about temperature's effect

Challenger
BY THE NUMBERS

SEVEN
members of crew – six
astronauts and one civilian

143,000
gallons of liquid oxygen plus
383,000 gallons of liquid
hydrogen in the external
fuel tank

20X
more fuel by weight than the
Shuttle itself

56.1
metres from the rocket
motor nozzles to
the nosecone

1977
First approach and
landing tests of the
Enterprise prototype

135
Total number of
Shuttle missions

TWO
major disasters resulting in
the loss of crew

2011
Final Shuttle mission,
STS-135, to the ISS

"For a successful technology, reality must take precedence over public relations"

Richard Feynman

on the seals in a car carburettor that sparked the physicist's imagination. "Sally and I were really good buddies," he told *Popular Mechanics* in 2016. "She figured she could trust me to give me that piece of paper and not implicate her or the people at NASA who gave it to her, because they could all get fired. I wondered how I could introduce this information. I kept it a secret that she had given me that piece of paper until she died."

The commission concluded that the disaster was an internal NASA matter, and that the agency could be left to address it with no need for a reduction in funding or a grounding of the Shuttle fleet. Feynman was so angered by this that his dissenting opinion was almost dropped from the report, eventually appearing as an appendix to the main body. He raged against NASA management, writing: "It appears that there are enormous differences of opinion as to the probability of a failure with loss of vehicle and of human life. The higher figures come from the

working engineers, and the very low figures from management.

"For a successful technology," he concluded, "reality must take precedence over public relations, for nature cannot be fooled." He would go on to suggest he had been led to the damning evidence by either NASA personnel or contractors. A second report into the disaster - carried out by the US House Committee on Science and Technology in late 1986 - agreed broadly with Rogers, but placed the blame on "poor technical decision making over a period of several years by top NASA and contractor personnel, who failed to act decisively to solve the increasingly serious anomalies in the Solid Rocket Booster joints".

In response to the Rogers Commission's report, with its nine safety recommendations, NASA began a complete redesign of the Shuttle's solid rocket boosters, overseen by an independent review body. The launch schedule was reorganised to give more time between launches, and a new orbiter, Endeavour, was commissioned to replace Challenger. It was decided that expendable launch vehicles, rather than crewed Shuttles, would be used for commercial satellite deployment missions. After 32 months grounded, the next Shuttle mission - STS-26 using Discovery to deploy a data relay satellite - returned safely to Earth after four days in space in October 1988.

Many lessons were learned from the Challenger disaster, but it's telling that the report into the second Shuttle crash, that of Columbia in 2003, would conclude that NASA had failed to learn many of the lessons of Challenger. While the agency had set up an independent office for safety

Below:
Challenger
fuselage
display at
the Kennedy
Space Center
Visitor
Complex

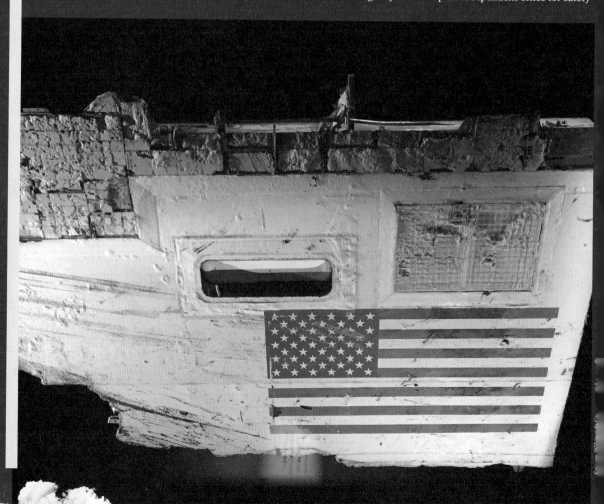

oversight as directed by the Rogers Commission, it did not meet the commission's intentions, and that decision making within NASA was still flawed.

The inclusion of McAuliffe on the crew, combined with the TV-friendly timing of the launch, meant that media coverage of the Challenger disaster was extensive, with many children watching the events play out. It's estimated that up to 17 per cent of the US population witnessed the disaster live on television, while 85 per cent knew about it within an hour. While NASA ended the program that saw civilians fly on Shuttle missions, Barbara Morgan, who was selected as McAuliffe's back-up on the Challenger mission, joined NASA and flew aboard Endeavour on the STS-118 mission to the International Space Station in 2007 as a mission specialist. She believes that despite the disaster, spaceflight is a worthwhile undertaking and should continue.

"Both Challenger and the Columbia have caused me to think, and it caused all of NASA to think," she said before the mission. "Kids were watching to see what the adults do in a terrible, terrible situation. What I thought was really important for kids to see is that we figure out what's wrong, we fix it and we move on, and we keep the future open for our young people."

Ian Evenden
Space science writer
Ian has been writing about the universe for over ten years, focusing on cosmology and space exploration. He's also a keen astrophotographer.

Below: Space Shuttle Challenger's STS-7 mission landed on 24 June 1983 at Edwards Air Force Base

Below: Debris from the forward skirt of Challenger's Solid Rocket Booster

© NASA

© NASA

Lessons NASA learned

One thing was clear following the Challenger disaster: crewed spaceflight could not stay the same

NEW JOINTS AND SEALING SYSTEM

Redesigned joints – which were already in production – and a new sealing system were implemented, with an inspection regime, in time for the next flight. This also added a third O-ring, and heaters to the joints.

SAFETY, RELIABILITY AND QUALITY ASSURANCE

The establishment of a new SR&QA office to oversee flight safety, though this did not go far enough to satisfy the Rogers Commission. The office reported directly to the NASA administrator.

CREW ESCAPE SYSTEM

The Crew Escape System was provided following the Challenger disaster. Previously the crew had no way of escaping their compartment. However, as the later Columbia disaster showed, it was only effective during level gliding flight.

Source: Wikipedia Commons © Robert Markowitz

FLIGHT RATE CHANGES

Commercial pressures had led to a Space Shuttle mission launch rate described as 'optimistic'. The removal of commercial satellite launch duties from the Shuttle program meant fewer Shuttle missions could be launched, with larger gaps between.

LANDING SAFETY

The final Challenger mission may never have landed, but among the recommendations of the Rogers Commission was an overhaul of the landing system, particularly in the brakes and nose wheel steering system, as well as the drag parachute that aided braking.

REORGANISATION OF NASA MANAGEMENT

The post of chief engineer was absorbed into the SR&QA office, while a new flight safety panel was established to set firmly defined policies and procedures that would ensure the uniform application of standards throughout the agency.

CHANGES IN DECISION MAKING

Following criticisms from the Rogers Commission, changes were made to the way decisions were made at NASA, with managers at Houston no longer able to waive safety concerns in Florida.

SPACEFLIGHT NO LONGER SEEN AS ROUTINE

America was almost bored with spaceflight in 1986, and this is part of what prompted McAuliffe to be on the Challenger mission. The representation of Shuttle missions needed to be changed to better represent the danger astronauts put themselves in.

All images © NASA unless stated otherwise

WHAT WE LEARNED FROM THE COLUMBIA DISASTER

How NASA was able to learn from a tragedy that took seven lives, and come back with a space programme more focused, and much safer, than ever before

Interviewed by Ian Evenden

©NASA

The US space shuttles were the world's first reusable spacecraft

"This day has brought terrible news and great sadness to our country," said President George W Bush in an address made on 1 February 2003." The Columbia is lost, there are no survivors." Seven astronauts lost their lives as the Space Shuttle Columbia, the first of NASA's fleet to fly and a veteran of 4,808 orbits of the Earth, broke up in the skies above Texas.

The cause of the disaster was damage to the shuttle's left wing, caused when a large piece of insulating foam fell from the external fuel tank on launch, leaving a hole in the reinforced carbon panels. Nearly 16 days later, as Columbia made its way back to Earth, superheated atmospheric gases, penetrated the wing and destroyed its internal structure. This led to a total loss of control, causing the shuttle to break apart as it travelled at over 18-times the speed of sound.

Following the loss of Columbia, NASA overhauled its safety procedures, changing everything from the astronauts' seats to the very position in which future spacecraft will sit in on their launch vehicles. The changes went deeper into NASA culture too, with the Engineering and Safety Center performing testing and analysis on every mission.

Shuttles shedding foam on launch - particularly the foam from the bipod ramp, a purely aerodynamic part of the thermal protection system (TPS) where the shuttle joins the main external fuel tank - had happened before. Back in 1983, the shuttle Challenger completed its mission successfully despite losing bipod ramp foam, and even survived window damage from being struck by space debris while in orbit. Further examples of foam shedding were logged over the next 20 years, including a 2002 Atlantis launch - a construction mission for the ISS - which had been carrying an external camera to look out for just this sort of thing.

Despite this, in 2003 the shuttle's controllers deemed it an acceptable risk. As the astronaut Gus Grissom, who died in the Apollo 1 fire, said back in 1965: "If we die, we want people to accept it. The conquest of space is worth the risk of life."

The leading edges of the shuttle's wings were coated in reinforced carbon-carbon, or RCC, a material noted for its heat-proof properties, which is also used in the nose cones of nuclear missiles and the brakes of Formula One cars. While it's less brittle than some ceramic materials, it still doesn't have a high degree of impact resistance.

Following the loss of Columbia, the Southwest Research Institute in San Antonio, Texas, used an air cannon to fire foam blocks at RCC panels from the leading edges of the wings of Discovery, having flown 30 missions and Atlantis, who had 27 previous missions. Under this bombardment, a crack appeared in Discovery's panel and a substantial hole appeared in Atlantis' panel. This clearly demonstrated the effect of a foam impact.

Back on the mission, with Columbia safely in orbit, another decision was made. Despite requests from engineers, shuttle managers chose not to examine the exterior of the shuttle photographically, which could have involved ground-based telescopes and the cameras of

The casualties

Ilan Ramon
Payload specialist

David M. Brown
Mission Specialist

Kalpana Chawla
Mission Specialist

Rick D. Husband
Commander

Michael P. Anderson
Payload Commander

Laurel Blair Salton Clark
Mission Specialist

William C. McCool
Pilot

Columbia in orbit in 1995, about to deploy the Microgravity Laboratory-2 from its cargo bay

Department of Defense spy satellites, or sending the astronauts on an EVA. Instead, NASA modelled the foam strike mathematically, but didn't reach a firm conclusion as to whether there had actually been any damage.

The assessment was that there was nothing that could have been done. Writing in 2013, retired NASA Space Shuttle Program deputy manager N. Wayne Hale recalled something said by Jon C. Harpold, the director of mission operations: "There is nothing we can do about damage to the TPS. If it has been damaged it's probably better not to know. I think the crew would rather not know. Don't you think it would be better for them to have a happy successful flight and die unexpectedly during entry than to stay on orbit, knowing that there was nothing to be done, until the air ran out?" Hale continues: "That mindset was widespread. Astronauts agreed."

Linda Ham, who led the mission management team for the STS-107 mission, spoke at the time of how this decision was made: "We were all trying to do the right thing. All along, we were basing our decisions on the best information that we had at the time," she said. "None of us felt that the analysis [of the foam strike] was faulty." "At the time, we had no indication or belief that there was anything here that was going to affect the crew, even in the long run," added Phil Engelauf, the mission operations representative on the management team.

In the appendices to the report of the Columbia Accident Investigation Board (CAIB), however, there's a modestly titled document "STS-107 In-Flight Options Assessment" that suggests an alternative scenario if the damage to Columbia had been identified. The

3 **17:39 UTC (Approximate)**
Video of the launch is reviewed and reveals nothing unusual. However, a high-resolution film was developed overnight does show the foam strike, but the low-res tracking camera cannot pick out the exact location of the damage.

2 **15:40:22 UTC**
A piece of insulating foam the size of a suitcase breaks off the launcher's external fuel tank, hitting the shuttle on its left wing.

Minute by minute: Columbia's final moments

As the Space Shuttle flew across the Californian coast, its fate had already been sealed

10 **13:59:32 UTC**
A final voice transmission – cut off halfway through a word – is received from the shuttle. Hydraulic pressure is lost five seconds later, meaning a total loss of control.

1 **16 January 2003, 15:39:00 UTC**
STS-107 launches from pad LC-39A at Kennedy Space Center, Florida. Columbia's 28th mission, it was delayed 18 times since its original launch date of 11 January 2001.

11 **14:00:18 UTC**
Eyewitnesses report the shuttle's disintegration over Texas. 39 seconds later, the crew module is seen to break up. A loud boom is heard.

4 **1 February 2003, 13:10 UTC**
The crew of the shuttle, after almost 16 days, are given the go signal for their reentry engine burn and complete the manoeuvre at 13:15:30 UTC.

6 **13:48:39 UTC**
Sensors on the left wing are showing strain levels higher than those seen on previous Columbia flights. Crossing the California coast at 13:53:26 UTC, the wing edges reach an estimated 1,538°C.

Crew seats
Ejection seats aren't practical at the high speeds of the shuttle, so the escape system consisted of a pole slid out to clear the orbiter's left wing, from where the astronauts could parachute into the sea. It required a stable glide, which the damaged Columbia was unable to provide.

5 **13:44:09 UTC**
Columbia enters the Earth's atmosphere, 400,000 feet above the Pacific Ocean. Over the next six minutes, the temperature of the leading wing edges begins to rise to about 1,371°C. This is normal.

Bipod ramp
Designed to help with both aerodynamics and thermal protection, the insulating foam was prone to detaching and falling under the stresses of launch.

Wing leading edge
Made of a brittle, but extremely heat-resistant material, the impact of foam hitting the wing was enough to make a hole that allowed superheated gases inside during reentry.

8 **13:54:24 UTC**
Sensors in the left wing appear not to be functioning. A bright flash is seen as the shuttle passes over the California-Nevada border.

9 **13:56:45 UTC**
Columbia, travelling at over 25,800kph, begins a planned roll manoeuvre above New Mexico. 18 more bright flashes are seen by watchers on the ground.

Crew suits
Introduced in 1994, the bright-orange Advanced Crew Escape Suit was worn for reentry. The CAIB found that Columbia's suits all failed at some point. However, none of the crew had time to seal their helmets, and some weren't wearing their gloves.

7 **13:53:46 UTC**
Ground observers report debris being shed from the shuttle. The trail it leaves in the sky brightens, appearing as a red streak on weather radar.

© NASA, Adrian Mann, Tobias Roetsch.

Lessons NASA learned

Much can be drawn from the CAIB report and the wreckage of the shuttle, and NASA wasn't slow in putting them into practice

International cooperation

Following the retirement of the shuttle fleet, NASA has had to rely on the Russian space agency to access the International Space Station. Orion itself is an international project, with the European Space Agency providing its service module.

Commercial spaceflight is OK

After Columbia, NASA developed a programme of commercial flights to the ISS, from companies such as SpaceX and Orbital Sciences. These are unmanned cargo flights, but crew-carrying commercial launches are planned.

Roundworms are really tough

A live group of roundworms, around 1mm long and part of an experiment carried out in orbit, survived the Columbia crash. Some of their descendants returned to space in 2011 aboard the shuttle Endeavour.

Modified reentry suit

The ACES suit was to be replaced by the Constellation space suit, but following the cancellation of that programme ACES has been modified for greater mobility and life-support capabilities.

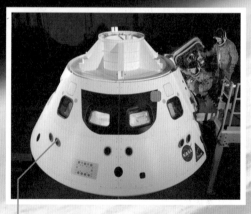

Whole new space capsule

"It is in the nation's interest to replace the shuttle as soon as possible," read the report of the CAIB. Announced in 2004, the Orion Crew Exploration Vehicle was a reaction to the recommendations.

Life support redesign
In the Columbia-era shuttle life-support system, an astronaut with his or her helmet's visor locked in the up position wasn't receiving any oxygen. This has been changed to ensure a constant flow of breathable gas to the helmet wearer.

The importance of research
Staff from NASA's Langley Research Center were on hand for all of the post-Columbia shuttle launches, and thermal protection repair kits, developed at the Virginia aeronautics lab, were carried on every subsequent mission.

Orion sits at top of rocket
By sitting on top of the launch vehicle, Orion cannot be hit by falling debris. This simple change, a return to the configuration of pre-shuttle launches, elegantly solves the problem of damage.

shuttle Atlantis was being prepared for launch, but its ISS resupply mission was still six weeks away. If the preparation process could be accelerated, if NASA would allow Atlantis to launch, and if the crew of the Columbia could stretch their life-support systems and power reserves long enough, then an in-orbit rescue was feasible, if challenging. Atlantis would have to fly, rendezvous with Columbia and carry out the rescue with a minimal crew of four, then return safely carrying the weight of 11 people, leaving no margin for error in a vehicle realistically designed for a maximum of seven.

NASA would also have had to reprogram Atlantis' computers to dock with a shuttle rather than the ISS, and invent spacewalk procedures for the actual rescue. Then the astronauts would have to learn these new skills in just two weeks. It was ambitious, to say the least.

The report dismissed a further option - sending Columbia to dock with the habitable but still-under-

> "All along, we were basing our decisions on the best information that we had at the time" Linda Ham

construction ISS. Unfortunately, physics got in the way, requiring much more fuel than Columbia had available to carry out the plane-change manoeuvre that would have pushed it into the station's orbit. "Columbia's 39-degree orbital inclination could not have been altered to the ISS's 51.6-degree inclination without approximately 12,600 ft/sec of translational capability," the report says. "Columbia had 448 ft/sec of propellant available."

All of this is hypothetical, however. The decision-making process that discounted the significance of the foam shedding and chose not to inspect the shuttle is described as 'flawed' in the CAIB report, which also points out similarities to the Challenger disaster 17 years earlier, when hot exhaust burned through two O-rings in a joint and ignited the external fuel tank shortly after launch. The Rogers Commission, which investigated the earlier shuttle explosion, determined that NASA's internal culture and an environment of overconfidence prevented safety concerns from reaching the top decision makers, and that pressure to maintain the launch schedule had led to poor choices being made.

The clearest parallel between the two shuttle losses, however, was that NASA had long known about a problem with the rings, but that increasing levels of damage to them had been tolerated over time, based on the rationale that nothing bad had happened yet. Likewise, foam and other debris had been falling during shuttle launches since the beginning, but it took until 2003 for something 'bad' to happen.

Teams combed Texas and Louisiana for debris, organising what they found on a grid painted on the floor of the shuttle's hangar. Eventually more than 84,000 pieces of Columbia were recovered, representing some 38 per cent of the shuttle. Tellingly, there is a lot more debris from the right wing than from the left, the plasma generated by reentry having burned away the aluminium alloy used for the internal struts. Of the 137 rolls of photographic film carried on the shuttle, 21 were recovered and developed.

Following the commission's report, NASA immediately put what it had learned from the investigation into practice. Speaking at the time, NASA administrator Sean O'Keefe said: "The findings and recommendations of the Columbia Accident Investigation Board will serve as NASA's blueprint. We already have begun to take action... and we intend to comply with the full range of recommendations."

And they did. Following the loss of Columbia, and the 29 months the shuttles were grounded, there was a change in the shuttle programme. All but one of the remaining missions, before the fleet's retirement in 2011, were to the International Space Station, which was hoped could offer a safe haven for astronauts whose orbiter had suffered damage while a rescue mission was scrambled.

The odd mission out was a 2009 trip to the Hubble Space Telescope by Atlantis, adding new instruments and replacing batteries, sensors and gyroscopes. It's interesting because its trajectory meant it was in greater danger than usual of

One of shuttle Columbia's main engine powerheads found on the grounds of Fort Polk, Louisiana

A memorial plaque mounted on the back of the high-gain antenna on the Mars rover Spirit

"The findings and recommendations of the Columbia Accident Investigation Board will serve as NASA's blueprint" Sean O'Keefe

encountering orbital debris. In keeping with the new focus on safety and damage assessment after Columbia's loss, a US Navy NP-3D Orion aircraft outfitted with a long-range infrared camera was deployed to track the shuttle in flight.

Focusing on an object flying at 15-times the speed of a bullet, while aboard a moving aircraft, would prove quite tricky – as flight operations lead Steve Tack explains: "You only have one shot. It's not like you can ask them to go around again and give us another try. It's a really exciting time, that 30 to 40 seconds when the shuttle is just screaming past us at Mach 15 and we're making a really hard turn to maintain tracking on it."

The first launch following the resumption of the programme was the shuttle Discovery on 26 July 2005. Having delivered supplies and a new module to the ISS, Discovery would go on to land safely – the only casualty being a bird that flew into the top of the rocket 2.5 seconds after ignition. However, 127.1 seconds after liftoff, debris was seen to fall from the external fuel tank. Luckily it did not hit the shuttle, but

frighteningly another piece, around 20 seconds later, did.

As part of the recommendations made by the Columbia Accident Investigation Board, Discovery was carrying an Orbiter Boom Sensor System (OBSS) – a 50-foot space selfie stick that was held by the shuttle's robot arm and used a combination of cameras and lasers to scan vulnerable parts of the shuttle after it entered orbit. As a further precaution, the shuttle executed a backflip manoeuvre before docking so it could be photographed from the ISS. No damage was seen, but NASA suspended shuttle flights again until the foam problem could be solved. It would be almost a year until the next shuttle launch.

The seven crew members lost with Columbia included the first Israeli in space, fighter pilot Ilan Ramon, as well as experienced astronauts, scientists and former US Air Force and Navy personnel. A lasting tribute came in the form of seven asteroids, discovered in July 2001: 51823 Rickhusband, 51824 Mikeanderson, 51825 Davidbrown, 51826 Kalpanachawla, 51827 Laurelclark, 51828 Ilanramon and 51829 Williemccool all orbit the Sun in the asteroid belt, between Mars and Jupiter. "Asteroids have been around for billions of years and will remain for billions more," said Dr Raymond Bambery, principal investigator of the NASA Jet Propulsion Laboratory's Near-Earth Asteroid Tracking Project. "I like to think that in the years, decades and millennia ahead, people will look to the heavens, locate these seven celestial sentinels and remember the sacrifice made by the Columbia astronauts."

Along with those asteroids, many statues and the Columbia Memorial Station on Mars, a memorial stone to the Columbia crew stands in the Arlington National Cemetery, Virginia, also home to a memorial to the crew of the shuttle Challenger, lost in 1986. Perhaps a greater tribute to the lives lost is the continuation of the space programme, as President Bush said in his address after the Columbia's destruction: "The cause in which they died will continue... our journey into space will go on."

The grid on the floor of the Reusable Launch Vehicle Hangar at Kennedy Space Center as workers in the field bring in pieces of Columbia's debris

Columbia: the key to our mission to Mars

The lessons learned from the disaster are still being applied today, nowhere more so than in the design of the Orion capsule

New launcher
The Space Launch System that will push Orion on its way to deep space use the engines from the Space Shuttle programme, but is claiming the title of most powerful rocket ever built. It's developed from the solid rocket boosters that propelled shuttles and their external fuel tanks skyward.

New docking procedures
Orion will be able to dock automatically like that on Russian Progress spacecraft (sources are unclear as to whether it will play the Blue Danube). In the shuttle, docking was in fact an all-manual affair.

New shielding
Orion's heat shield is supported by titanium trusses, and its composite material surface is further protected with an ablative coating – it's designed to wear away as it experiences extreme temperatures.

New positioning
By placing the crew capsule on top of the launcher, rather than slung by its side, there's no way it can be struck by falling debris, even if it does occur.

New spacesuits
Columbia's crew were killed when their crew capsule depressurised, even before it broke apart. Orion's space suits will instantly and automatically inflate to protect from a loss of air pressure.

New seats
The seats and seatbelts used by the astronauts in Orion are different to those in the shuttle. New, form-fitting designs are tailored to each astronaut, and the belts adjust to a range of sizes.

New small thinking
If the Orion service module was about 60cm less in diameter, it could fit in the Space Shuttle cargo bay. It's a mere eight metres long, compared to the shuttle's 37.2 metres.

New computers
The CPUs powering Orion's computers are from 2002 – your smartphone likely has more raw power. But your phone doesn't have radiation shielding, extra-strong circuit boards or vibration-resistant connectors.

New old landing system
Orion will splash down in the ocean, just like the Mercury, Gemini and Apollo capsules did. It will be picked up by a Navy amphibious transport dock – a ship with an enormous well deck that can be manoeuvred below the floating capsule.

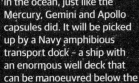

New escape system
The Launch Abort System will separate the crew module from the rest of Orion, and can be activated within milliseconds, if needed.

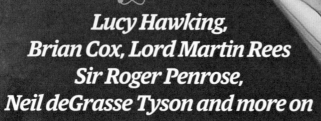

Lucy Hawking,
Brian Cox, Lord Martin Rees
Sir Roger Penrose,
Neil deGrasse Tyson and more on

Remembering
THE WORLD'S GREATEST SCIENTIST

A ny discussion of Stephen Hawking's remarkable life is necessarily a binary one. There's his body of work, perhaps unmatched among modern physicists, and there is the man himself, instantly recognisable thanks to his wheelchair and distinctive computer-generated voice.

Combined, they provide the evocative image of a mind voyaging among the stars despite the frustrations imposed by its body, and Hawking's story is one of such triumph against the odds that it's almost impossible to separate the two threads.

Born 8 January 1942, exactly 300 years after the death of Galileo, Stephen William was the eldest of Frank and Isobel Hawking's four children, with two younger sisters and an adopted brother. His parents both studied at Oxford, his father reading medicine and his mother philosophy, politics and economics. His father's work in parasitology frequently took him to Africa. He was there at the outbreak of WWII, and took a journey across the continent to meet a ship bound for England; despite his attempts to volunteer for military service, his medical research was deemed more important. The family settled in St Albans, Hertfordshire, where their habit of travelling in a converted London taxi and spending mealtimes in silence, all reading books, gained them a reputation for eccentricity. They owned a former gypsy caravan parked in a field near Weymouth, Dorset, as a holiday home, until the county council removed it.

Sent to a 'progressive' school in Highgate, London, that failed to teach him to read (he finally managed it aged eight) Hawking nevertheless passed his Eleven Plus exam a year early and attended independent schools in Hertfordshire. His father's wish that he attend the prestigious Westminster School didn't come to fruition, as Hawking was ill on the day of the scholarship exam that would have allowed his parents to afford its fees. When not at school, Hawking spent his teenage years playing with model trains, none of which worked very well, and building toy aircraft and boats. "My aim was always to build working models that I could control," Hawking wrote. "I didn't care what they looked like." He also created complicated games with a friend, including a war game played on a board with 4,000 squares. "I think these games, as well as the trains, boats and airplanes, came from an urge to know how systems worked and how to control them. If you understand how the universe operates, you control it, in a way."

Though not initially successful in his studies Hawking showed a flair for the sciences and, having picked up the nickname 'Einstein', chose to study physics and chemistry at University College Oxford - the same college his father, who wanted him to study medicine, had attended - aged just 17.

Physics, described by Hawking as "the most boring subject at school because it was so easy and obvious", became more interesting to him, despite chemistry's potential for unexpected explosions, because it "offered the hope of understanding where we came from and why we are here". It came naturally to him, his physics tutor, Robert Berman, remarking: "It was

A brief history of Hawking

1959
Begins studying at University College, Oxford, aged 17.

1962
Becomes a doctoral student at Cambridge under Dennis Sciama.

1963
Diagnosed with amyotrophic lateral sclerosis following a fall while ice skating.

1970
With Penrose, publishes a proof that the universe must have begun as a singularity.

1973
Publishes his first academic book, *The Large Scale Structure of Space-Time*, co-written with George Ellis.

1974
Elected a Fellow of the Royal Society, several weeks after the announcement of Hawking radiation.

1979
Elected Lucasian Professor of Mathematics at the University of Cambridge.

1981
Proposes that information in a black hole is irretrievably lost when a black hole evaporates, igniting a 'black hole war' with Susskind and 't Hooft.

1984
First draft of *A Brief History of Time* completed. Publisher thinks it's too technical.

1985
Contracts pneumonia and undergoes a tracheotomy. Loses power of speech.

1988
A Brief History of Time published. The book goes on to sell over ten million copies worldwide.

1988
Jointly with Penrose, wins the Wolf Prize in Physics worth $100,000, "for their brilliant development of the theory of general relativity".

1989
Appointed a Companion of Honour in the Birthday Honours, but turns down a knighthood.

1991
A film version of *A Brief History of Time*, produced by Steven Spielberg, premieres.

1997
A six-part documentary series, *Stephen Hawking's Universe*, is made.

2004
Admits he was on the wrong side in the 'black hole war', and buys Preskill an encyclopedia.

2005
Writes *A Briefer History of Time* with Leonard Mlodinow to update his ideas and make them more accessible.

2007
Publishes *George's Secret Key to the Universe* with his daughter Lucy.

2009
Holds party for time travellers. None show up.

2009
Receives Presidential Medal of Freedom from Barack Obama.

© Dimitrios Kambouris/Getty; NASA, ESA, and The Hubble Heritage

be done, and he could do it without looking to see how other people did it."

Being much younger than his peers, many of whom had come to university after doing military service, Hawking stood apart, feeling rather lonely. He joined the university rowing club (something he described as "fairly disastrous"), suffering head-on collisions, disqualification and eventually coxing a crew through dangerous waters that led to the boat getting damaged. He cultivated interests in music and science fiction and made friends, but experienced clumsiness that led to falls and difficulty with rowing.

An anti-work culture at Oxford at the time led to problems when it came to Hawking's final exams. Having calculated he carried out just 1,000 hours of study over the three years of his degree, Hawking was unprepared and planned to answer only some of the questions. Despite this he placed right on the border between first- and second-class honours, using a viva examination in which he promised to leave Oxford for Cambridge if awarded a first to tip himself over in to the higher category.

In 1962 Hawking kept his word and joined Trinity Hall college, Cambridge, as a doctoral student. He applied to work with Fred Hoyle - the astronomer whose 1954 paper launched stellar nucleosynthesis, the study of how stars fuse elements to create heat and light - but was disappointed to be assigned to Dennis Sciama, a physicist he was unfamiliar with. Today considered one of the fathers of modern cosmology, Sciama is known for his work on radio astronomy, dark matter, quasars, the cosmic background radiation, black holes and general relativity. In addition to Hawking his students have included Lord Martin Rees, the Astronomer Royal; quantum computing pioneer David Deutsch; emeritus distinguished professor of complex systems at the University of Cape Town George Ellis and Oxford University professor of physics James Binney.

Having not studied mathematics since he left school Hawking found cosmology and general relativity a struggle, but they were the areas he was determined to work in. His alternative field, the study of elementary particles, was too much like "botany" for his tastes, and many of the prevailing theories of the time turned out to be wrong. "I'm very glad I didn't start my research into elementary particles," Hawking wrote later. "None of my work from that period would have survived."

Hawking's clumsiness became more of an issue during his time at Cambridge. After being told by a doctor he should drink less, it took an incident while ice skating at Christmas for him to be referred to a specialist. After two weeks of tests all that he was told was that his condition wasn't multiple sclerosis, but that he was an atypical case, and he didn't ask for more details. Eventually he was told he had amyotrophic lateral sclerosis (ALS), a form of motor neurone disease characterised by gradually worsening muscle weakness, and given two years to live. This was 1963, and he was just 21.

It is often reported that Hawking became depressed and began drinking heavily at this time, but he denies this, admitting to little worse than listening to Wagner. "Before my condition was diagnosed," he wrote, "I had been very bored with life. But shortly after I came out of the hospital... I

Hawking's daughter: Lucy Hawking
"We will miss him forever"

"My father used to just cause absolute consternation. People would just stop and stare - my father had his own electric wheelchair, which he used to drive at great speed across the whole of Cambridge, accompanied by me and my two older brothers, sort of like blonde little moppets running alongside with our ice creams - I think in horror, amazement and shock. How was this disabled man by himself? What were these children doing? People just couldn't process the sight. My father always had lots of scientific colleagues who would come for dinner pretty much every night and they would discuss extraordinary topics. No topics were out of bounds. As a child, you could ask any question you wanted and get a reply. It was my son's eight or ninth birthday party and one of my son's friends went up to my dad and asked: 'Stephen, what would happen to me if I fell into a black hole?' Everyone was really interested and everyone waited for the answer. My father told him that he would be turned into spaghetti and of course, all the kids were thrilled and they totally understood his answer, and the adults pretended to.

"People who live in really extreme circumstances, for example in war zones, seemed to find something very, very inspirational in his example of perseverance and persistence and his kind of ability to rise above his suffering and still want to communicate at a higher level with humour to a world population. Some children knew him as a genius, others knew him as a disabled man.

"His courage and persistence with his brilliance and humour inspired people across the world. He once said, 'It would not be much of a universe if it wasn't home to the people you love'. We will miss him forever."

Hawking was diagnosed with amyotrophic lateral sclerosis (ALS) during his early life

Hawking predicted that radiation is leaked by black holes

Hawking theory #1
Black holes leak radiation

THEORY PROVEN? **NO**

Hawking's most famous theoretical discovery, and one he was sad not to have won a Nobel Prize for, although he conceded it was hard to test experimentally. The radiation is predicted to be released by black holes, and can cause them to eventually evaporate if they're not kept topped up with new matter and energy. In September 2010, an experiment at a lab in Italy produced a result that looked very much like Hawking radiation, but remains unverified. NASA's Fermi Space Telescope, however, may yet provide the proof that's needed as it hunts for gamma ray flashes. Sadly, Nobel prizes are not awarded posthumously.

Calculations for Hawking's theory of 'Hawking radiation'

spherical, but Hawking realised that the same argument could be applied to the whole universe, and this proved that space-time had a beginning. The thesis' acceptance in 1966, along with a fellowship grant from a Cambridge college, allowed Hawking to get married to Jane and eventually buy a house, although the increasing weakness of his muscles was making it harder for him to walk and give lectures. Then in May 1967, their first child, Robert, was born.

Hawking's work on singularities continued, and working together with Penrose he published a proof that the universe must have started as one if it also satisfies a few other conditions. The 1970s proved to be a fruitful period for his mind, beginning with the second law of black hole dynamics - that a black hole's event horizon cannot shrink - in 1970, then four more laws of black hole mechanics in association with other academics. His daughter Lucy was also born that year. He published an award-winning essay on black holes in 1971, and his first book, *The Large Scale Structure of Space-Time*, written with George Ellis and dedicated to Sciama, was published in 1973. Hawking would go on to describe the book as "highly technical" and wrote: "I would caution the general reader against attempting to consult it." Despite this, it has been reprinted several times.

The year 1973 also saw a shift in Hawking's work as he became more interested in quantum mechanics, particularly where the theory intersects with gravity, following a visit to Moscow where he met Yakov Borisovich Zel'dovich and Alexei

realised that there were a lot of worthwhile things I could do." He returned to his work, the disease progressing much more slowly than doctors had predicted, and became engaged to Jane Wilde. "This gave me something to live for," he wrote.

A great debate in physics at the time was the Big Bang theory - the one we're familiar with today in which the universe has a defined beginning - versus the Steady State theory, which held that the universe had always been the way it is, with the continuous creation of matter allowing it to remain that way despite the universe's observable expansion. Hoyle was a major proponent of the Steady State, and while Sciama initially supported

it he would abandon the theory when the evidence mounted against it. Hawking publicly challenged Hoyle over his new theory of gravity at a 1964 Royal Society lecture, appearing to calculate in his head something he had in fact had time to work on, as he had been sharing an office with Hoyle's student and read a draft of the lecture. Hoyle was furious, but would later offer Hawking a job.

First, though, he needed to finish his PhD. He wrote a thesis on singularity theory inspired by the work of Roger Penrose, now the emeritus Rouse Ball professor of mathematics at the University of Oxford. Penrose showed that a star would collapse into a singularity even if it wasn't perfectly

---

© Andre Pattenden; The Royal Society; University of Cambridge

Fellow physicist: Professor Brian Cox

"One of the great things about Stephen was that he became quite political"

"He is rightly described as one of the great scientists, and that's for several reasons. His initial paper was on Einstein's theory of general relativity, published in 1915 and what we understand to be the framework of the universe. And he proved that, given just that theory, there has to be an origin of time. So, he essentially proved that not long after his thesis - it was part of his thesis at Cambridge and called the singularity theorem. Hawking then moved on to black holes, proving that they're not entirely black. A common picture of a black hole is that when you throw something into it, it never comes back. Nothing can escape, not even light. But Hawking showed that that wasn't right. He showed that they have a temperature and they glow and that they radiate out into space and ultimately, over really long times, they evaporate away, and that's called Hawking

radiation. Hawking took us to the next step in proving Einstein's theory of relativity; it's the next step to the theory we hope is there - it's the theory we need to understand the universe. It's like what Hawking said beautifully at the end of *A Brief History of Time*: he said, 'If we know all of this, we'll know the mind of God'. But of course he was talking about nature there, he wasn't a religious man. Einstein used to talk in a similar way. They both believed there's an idea, a regularity and beauty that underpins the universe.

"I got to know Stephen later in life and he was very funny. One thing I did with him was Monty Python at the O2. Eric Idle asked me if I could get Stephen to do a sketch with them so I emailed him, and within about a minute an email came back from Stephen saying yes. We went down to Cambridge for it. I'm always criticising in a

gentle way Eric's songs because they're not really accurate. There's a song called the Galaxy Song which talks about the Earth going around the Sun in a circle. And I say it's not a circle, it's an ellipse. It's scientifically inaccurate. So Eric came up with this sketch where I would be criticising the *Galaxy Song* and then in the background, there is a speck coming past King's College and it's Stephen in his wheelchair and he runs me over and says, 'I think you're being pedantic', and Stephen starts singing the *Galaxy Song*. The 'I think you're being pedantic' was an ad lib and he did it with perfect comic timing. At the time, he was finding it very difficult to type things into his computer. He was very funny, he wasn't in any way some dusty scientist.

"I have to say that one of the great things about Stephen was

that he became quite political. He talked about how valuable science is as a way of thinking, a humble and careful way of thinking, and how our future should be bright - there are a lot of things to do and understand as individuals and as members of the human race. In order to do that, we have to think about our position in the universe as one civilisation. He became very active in putting over that point of view; he [often questioned] how can science influence how we behave. I think that was extremely important, he had a big voice. He also pointed out [humanity's] stupidity; how we had the tendency to look inwards rather than outwards with our petty internal conflicts rather than thinking about our wider value."

Starobinsky, who had shown that rotating black holes emit particles, breaking the second law of black hole dynamics. In 1974 Hawking was able to show - controversially at the time - that black holes emit radiation, something now known as Hawking radiation, which if not replenished can cause a black hole to evaporate. The same year he was elected a Fellow of the Royal Society, one of the youngest to receive the honour at the time.

It's worth noting that, at the time, there was no observational evidence for black holes - they existed purely in the theoretical work of various physicists. Hawking's sense of humour frequently shone through the complex nature of his professional life, and the bets he made during his career, often planning to lose them, are a good example of this. In 1974 he bet the American physicist Kip Thorne that Cygnus X-1, a strong X-ray source around 6,100 light years from the Sun, wasn't a black hole. The bet wasn't for money, however. Thorne's wager was a four-year subscription to *Private Eye*, while Hawking put up a single year's worth of *Penthouse* magazine, calling the bet an "insurance policy" in case all his work on black holes was wrong - at least he'd have something to read. By 1990 there

Hawking's successor: Michael Green
"It's going to be difficult to live up to him"

"Stephen Hawking's name carries a certain weight with it and it's extremely difficult to imagine one would live up to it [Green will take over as Lucasian Professor of Mathematics at Cambridge]. His name comes up all the time; he had an influence on my work. He pinpointed an interface between general relativity, statistical mechanics and thermodynamics and quantum mechanics, and he put them all together. It raised the possibility of a very ambitious

meta-unification of ideas and, at the same time, it raised some puzzles. Black holes appear to be, in some senses, like quantum mechanical objects, but in some senses they seem to violate our ideas about quantum mechanics.

"Perhaps it's because of the fact he's so physically restricted, or perhaps it would have been the case anyway, but there's a certain quality to the way he works and the style of results he produces which is very different from the run-of-the-

mill theoretical physics paper.

"His work has been dramatically important in several instances over a long period of time. Added to that is this extraordinary physical handicap, and the fact that he's able to do anything is remarkable. If I get a headache, I can't work, but he seemed to be able to produce stuff despite fantastic problems."

The universe is widely accepted to have begun from the Big Bang

THEORY YES PROVEN?

Hawking theory #2
The universe began as a single point

General relativity predicts its own limitations, particularly in situations such as the gravitational collapse of massive stars or the conditions at the very beginning of the universe. Hawking and Penrose's work, among other things, predicts that the universe must have begun with a singularity - an area of infinite gravity. To the non-physicist, the theorems are a load of complicated maths, but they're held to be seminal work by the cosmological community, and go on to deal with subjects like whether space is infinite, and whether the universe will one day contract.

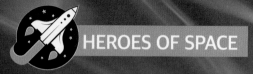

Hawking originally thought that black holes couldn't radiate - that is until he performed a lengthy calculation

THEORY · YES · PROVEN?

Hawking theory #3

The Bekenstein–Hawking formula

The second law of thermodynamics requires black holes to have entropy. Israeli-American physicist Jacob Bekenstein built on Hawking's work to show that the amount of entropy was proportional to the area of its event horizon, and was able to extend the second law to include black hole systems. Hawking originally opposed Bekenstein, claiming black holes could not radiate, but changed his mind after performing a lengthy calculation that led to the proposal of Hawking radiation.

Hawking celebrating 50 years as a fellow of Gonville & Caius College, Cambridge

Hawking's colleague: Sir Roger Penrose

"Being a student of his was not easy... he ran his wheelchair over the foot of a student who caused him irritation"

"Those who knew Hawking would clearly appreciate the dominating presence of a real human being with an enormous zest for life, great humour and tremendous determination, yet with normal human weaknesses, as well as his more obvious strengths. It seems clear that he took great delight in his commonly perceived role as 'the #1 celebrity scientist'; huge audiences would attend his public lectures, perhaps not always just for edification.

"[In the scientific community] he was extremely highly regarded in view of his many greatly impressive, sometimes revolutionary contributions to the understanding of the physics and the geometry of the universe. Despite being diagnosed shortly after his 21st birthday as suffering from a then-unspecified incurable disease, he didn't succumb to depression - as others might -

but began to set his sights on some of the most fundamental questions concerning the physical nature of the universe. In due course he would achieve extraordinary successes against the severest physical disabilities.

Defying established medical opinion, he managed to live another 55 years.

"He was an extraordinarily determined person. He would insist that he should do things for himself. This, in turn, perhaps kept his muscles active in a way that delayed their atrophy, thereby slowing the progress of the disease. Nevertheless, his condition continued to deteriorate until he had almost no movement left, and his speech could barely be made out at all except by a very few who knew him well. He contracted pneumonia while in Switzerland in 1985, and a tracheotomy was necessary to save his life. Strangely, after this brush with death the progress of his degenerative disease seemed to slow to a

virtual halt. His tracheotomy prevented any form of speech, however, so acquiring a computerised speech synthesiser became necessity.

"Hawking had many students, some of whom later made significant names for themselves. Yet being a student of his was not easy. He had been known to run his wheelchair over the foot of a student who caused him irritation.

"Despite his terrible physical circumstance, he almost always remained positive about life. He enjoyed his work, the company of other scientists, the arts, the fruits of his fame, his travels. He took great pleasure in children, sometimes entertaining them by swivelling around in his motorised wheelchair. Social issues concerned him. He promoted scientific understanding. He could be generous and was very often witty. He could display something of the arrogance that is not uncommon among physicists working at the cutting edge, and he had an autocratic streak, yet he could also show a true humility that is the mark of greatness."

"Hawking's sense of humour frequently shone through the complex nature of his professional life"

was so much evidence for black holes that Hawking conceded. Speaking in a 1997 TV documentary, Thorne alleged Hawking broke into his office and placed his thumbprint on the original handwritten bet, acknowledging he had lost. In the same film Hawking says with a grin: "I had given Thorne a subscription to *Penthouse*, much to his wife's disgust."

Thorne invited Hawking to the California Institute of Technology in Pasadena, where he encountered an electric wheelchair for the first time. Already notorious for the wild and erratic way he drove his manual wheelchair, and for illegally carrying passengers in his electric three-wheeled car, he enjoyed the extra independence the powered chair gave him. His links with Caltech stretch back to 1970 when he was appointed the Sherman Fairchild distinguished visiting professorship, and he spent a month there almost every year. He returned to Cambridge in 1975 to a new post, reader in gravitational physics, and began to attract recognition, winning the Eddington Medal from the Royal Astronomical Society and the Pius XI Gold Medal, presented by the Pope. He was minded to reject this latter honour, but recalled that the Vatican had pardoned Galileo. While in Italy he met Paul Dirac, one of the founders of quantum physics, who had told the Pontifical Academy of Sciences to award the medal to Hawking.

In 1974 Hawking was a research assistant. Three years later he progressed to professor of gravitational physics, and in 1979 he became the Lucasian Professor of Mathematics at Cambridge - a post founded in 1663 and once held by Dirac,

Charles Babbage and Sir Isaac Newton (and, if *Star Trek: The Next Generation* is to be believed, by Lt Cmdr Data in the 24th century). The Hawkings' third child, Tim, was also born around this time, but Hawking's ALS continued to worsen, the muscle weakness bringing on fits of choking. He accepted home nursing services reluctantly.

Changes also came in his work. His previous insistence on mathematical proofs became less important, and he became more speculative in his theoretical work. "I would rather be right than be rigorous," he famously said to Thorne, and returned to the subject in his later writings: "It is almost impossible to be rigorous in quantum physics, because the whole field is on very shaky mathematical ground." In 1981, his proposal that

Hawking visits the Temple of Heaven in Beijing in 2006

The world remembers a "brilliant and funny" man

The famous physicist is remembered by some of the world's greatest scientists, public figures and entertainers

"His passing has left an intellectual vacuum in his wake, but it's not empty. Think of it as a kind of vacuum energy permeating the fabric of space-time that defies measure."
Astrophysicist Neil deGrasse Tyson

"Have fun out there among the stars."
Former US President Barack Obama

"Stephen Hawking was the funniest man I have ever met."
Actor Eddie Redmayne

"With grace, wit and courage, his genius took us all to the very edge of space and time."
Physicist Brian Greene

"We will always be inspired by his life and ideas."
Apple CEO Tim Cook

"He had a wickedly funny sense of humour. He virtually created the publishing genre of popular science. I will miss our margaritas but will raise one to the stars to celebrate your life."
Actor Benedict Cumberbatch

"He inspired generations to look beyond our own blue planet and expand our understanding of the universe. His personality and genius will be sorely missed."
Astronaut Tim Peake

information, or the relationships between particles, contained in a black hole is lost when it evaporates - a violation of quantum mechanics - set off what sounds like the greatest sci-fi film never made, the 'black hole war', with physicists Leonard Susskind and Gerard 't Hooft. Quantum mechanics and relativity are fundamentally incompatible, and the debate led to 't Hooft's development of the holographic principle - that the information is preserved on the boundary of the system through bumps in the event horizon - that's now part of string theory.

Hawking's mind began to be occupied by the theory of the beginning of the universe. Cosmological inflation, the idea that the universe expanded extremely rapidly at first before slowing down, was new and exciting, and Hawking's work in this period suggested that before the Big Bang time simply didn't exist, and that while the universe has no boundaries it does have a shape. A consequence of this was explored in a 1985 paper that theorised that if the universe stopped expanding and began to collapse, time would run backwards. It was later withdrawn, but this didn't stop the flow of awards and recognition, with Hawking becoming a CBE. His ideas here led to work beginning on his book *A Brief History of Time*.

It was around this time that Hawking began using the speech-generating device that became such a recognisable part of his public image. Its American accent was the only one available on the early model, which ran on an Apple II computer, but even when other accents became available he chose to stick with the original, saying: "I keep it because I have not heard a voice I like better."

The incident that led to the loss of his speech was more serious, however. In 1985 Hawking was visiting CERN, the particle accelerator laboratory on the border of France and Switzerland, when he contracted life-threatening pneumonia. His condition deteriorated so badly that his wife was asked if she wanted to withdraw life support - she refused and had him flown by helicopter to Addenbrooke's Hospital in Cambridge, but a tracheotomy was carried out to help him breathe. This permanently took away his ability to speak. While he recovered he needed round-the-clock nursing care, and one of those employed was Elaine Mason, who would become his second wife.

The number of revisions required to make *A Brief History of Time* accessible to a non-specialist reader irritated Hawking, and he began using an assistant to help him finish writing it. Prior to this he had given lectures through an interpreter and written papers by dictating to a secretary, and he would go on to write several books using the speech synthesis program, which would be upgraded various times, moving from Apple systems to Intel.

A Brief History of Time cemented Hawking as one of the world's pre-eminent scientific minds.

"I wanted to explain how far I felt we had come in our understanding of the universe"

Prof Stephen Hawking

Hawking had first had the idea to write it in 1982, writing: "I wanted to explain how far I felt we had come in our understanding of the universe: how we might be near finding a complete theory that would describe the universe and everything in it." He chose the book's publisher, Bantam, because its books were widely available at airports, and was influenced by the BBC documentary series *The Ascent of Man*, which traced the development of human society. "I was sure that nearly everyone is interested in how the universe operates," he wrote, "but most people cannot follow mathematical equations. I don't care much for equations myself. I think in pictorial terms, and my aim in the book was to describe these mental images in words, with the help of familiar analogies and a few diagrams."

Published in 1988, the book would go on to sell over ten million copies worldwide. *Newsweek* featured Hawking on its cover, bestowing the title 'Master of the universe' on him, but it wasn't all plain sailing. Early copies of the book, including those sent out to publications for review, were riddled with errors, particularly in the labelling of photos and diagrams. The entire first printing was recalled and pulped, leading Hawking to quip that any surviving copies must be worth quite a lot of money. After an intense period of re-editing and checking, the book was released on April fool's day, and went on to spend a record-breaking 237 weeks on *The Times* best-seller list. While many media reviews concentrated on how remarkable it was

Hawking was awarded the Presidential Medal of Freedom on 12 August 2009

Hawking will forever be remembered as one of the greatest minds of the 20th century

"If you understand how the universe operates, you control it, in a way"

Prof Stephen Hawking

THEORY YES PROVEN?

Hawking theory #4

Hawking energy

Hawking energy is a possible definition of mass in general relativity - Einstein's framework doesn't supply a single definition of mass, but has several which become applicable under different circumstances. Hawking energy has to do with measuring how rays of light bend around a region of space which has a mass you want to define, and once again dissolves into a huge number of equations and symbols. It's an important tool for theoretical physicists, but a bit baffling to the rest of us.

Galaxy

Galaxy cluster

Distorted light rays

Lensed galaxy images

Earth

In 2007, Hawking experienced some four minutes of weightlessness in a modified Boeing jet

Hawking's CV in brief

2009-2018
Director of research, Cambridge University Department of Applied Mathematics and Theoretical Physics
Published more books; inspired a Hollywood movie; held a party for time travellers; received Presidential Medal of Freedom, Russian Special Fundamental Physics Prize, and honorary doctorate from Imperial College London.

1979-2009
Lucasian Professor of Mathematics at the University of Cambridge
Pushed boundaries of knowledge of black holes and the beginning of the universe. Published many books, including a ten-million seller and awarded the Copley medal.

1975-1979
Reader in gravitational physics, professor of gravitational physics, Gonville & Caius College, Cambridge
Published first book. Won Eddington, Hughes, Albert Einstein and Pius XI medals, plus the Dannie Heineman Prize and the Maxwell Prize. Honorary doctorate from University of Oxford.

1969-1975
Fellowship for distinction in science, Gonville & Caius College
A post created specially for him. Proposed laws of black hole mechanics. Discovered Hawking radiation.

1965-1969
Research fellow, Gonville & Caius College
Extended the concepts of the singularity theorem explored in PhD thesis, explored the idea that the universe may have begun as a singularity.

that a man with motor neurone disease could have written such a book, Hawking was flattered by one that compared it to Robert M. Pirsig's *Zen and the Art of Motorcycle Maintenance*, writing, "I hope that, like *Zen*, it gives people the feeling that they need not be cut off from the great intellectual and philosophical questions."

In the Queen's 1989 Birthday Honours, Hawking added the Order of the Companions of Honour to his CBE. The order is awarded for "having a major contribution to the arts, science, medicine or government lasting over a long period of time," but he turned down a knighthood because he "does not like titles" according to *The Telegraph*. He has also received 13 honorary degrees, the Paul Dirac medal (1987) and the Wolf Prize – the last one jointly with Penrose.

The books didn't stop coming, and neither did the bets. Kip Thorne, Hawking's friend from Caltech, was often his accomplice, and in 1991 he bet Thorne and John Preskill (also of Caltech) that Penrose was correct that singularities could not exist without an event horizon. He would concede this bet in 1997, then change his mind and replace the wager with one that had further conditions attached. Thorne also planted the idea in Hawking's mind that it

An image of Hawking is projected onto Cambridge University during its 800th anniversary light show

A scaled version of the observable universe by muscian and artist Pablo Carlos Budassi

Hawking theory #5

The Gibbons-Hawking effect

Developed with Cambridge physicist Gary Gibbons, the Gibbons-Hawking effect states that a temperature can be associated with solutions of the Einstein field equations (that's general relativity) that contain a causal horizon. This includes event horizons from black holes, but could also include the horizon of the visible universe. If black holes have a temperature, they must radiate, and this backs up the theory behind Hawking radiation.

might be possible to travel into the past through wormholes, and Hawking began investigating whether this was possible. It was a tricky area of research, however, because it was seen as a joke by many. "In physics circles, there are only a few of us foolhardy enough to work on a subject that some consider unserious or politically incorrect," wrote Hawking. "So we disguise our focus by using technical terms, such as 'particle histories that are closed', that are code for time travel."

Wormholes, which are yet to be proven to exist, would be useful for rapid space travel as well as popping back in time, and Hawking boiled the question down to whether space-time would "admit time-like curves that return to their starting point again and again." Many solutions to Einstein's equations suggest not, although the work of Kurt Gödel does provide a way around this. Hawking concluded that such closed space-time curves do not naturally occur in our universe, but that an advanced future civilisation could potentially build a time machine and come back to visit us. In 2009, to find out whether he was right, Hawking threw a party for time travellers with champagne, but sent the out invitations after it was over. Only people who could travel back in time would know to come.

Sadly no one came, and history does not record what happened to all the food, but another attempt was made to catch out time travellers living among us - the ballot for tickets to Hawking's memorial service in 2018 allowed would-be attendees to input a date of birth up to 2038. Hawking was resigned to the fact, however, that time traveller's weren't going

> ## "Thorne planted the idea in Hawking's mind that it might be possible to travel into the past"

Hawking's student: Fay Dowker

"His many awards, prizes and honours don't capture the magic that occurred around him"

"Stephen was my teacher, mentor and friend. I, like many who knew and loved him, had come to think of him as immortal, and our sorrow is tinged with a feeling of disbelief that he is no longer here. Robert, Lucy, Tim, members of the Hawking family, friends and carers of Stephen: it has been said, 'The arc of the moral universe is long, but it bends towards justice'. Stephen, in his life, worked to make it so. We can also say, 'The arc of the history of science is long, but it bends towards unity'. Stephen's place in that great history is eternal. Stephen shared his work and his zest for the fundamental questions it addressed with wide audiences. He inspired people with the excitement and importance of pure scientific enquiry and was admired and revered for his devotion, as a scholar, to the pursuit of knowledge. This high regard was demonstrated wherever in the world he gave a public lecture: the auditorium was always packed, the atmosphere electric and the applause thunderous."

Could information be destroyed when it falls into a black hole?

Hawking theory #6

Black hole information paradox

Whether or not information about matter and energy is destroyed when it falls into a black hole was a major debate, as a principle of quantum mechanics is that information about a system is encoded in its wave function. Hawking believed it would be destroyed, but ended up in a 'war' with two other physicists and eventually changed his mind, proposing in 2016 that information can move in and out of black holes using low-energy particles that exist in zero-energy space.

THEORY NO PROVEN?

to crash his party. "I don't think time travel will ever be possible," he wrote. "If it were, we would have been overrun by tourists from the future by now."

Through the 1990s and 2000s Hawking continued his work on black holes. Hawking radiation, the mechanism through which black holes could evaporate, was impossible under general relativity unless the mass-energy it carried came from somewhere outside the event horizon. This, however, contradicted quantum mechanics. One of the theories needed to change to account for this contradiction, and this led to another bet between the trio of Hawking, Thorne and Preskill over which was correct. The winner would receive an encyclopedia. The bet, placed in 1997, was lost in 2004 when Hawking conceded that event horizons could fluctuate, leaking energy and information that had fallen into the hole earlier, although it would be useless, publishing a paper on the subject in 2005. He bought Preskill a baseball encyclopedia, but joked that he should have burned it first to match the unreadable information found in Hawking radiation. He would go on to call this debate his "biggest blunder".

Another example of Hawking not quite getting everything right came in 2002, when he engaged in a debate with Peter Higgs over whether the Higgs boson - an elementary particle predicted by the standard model that gives other particles mass - would ever be discovered. Higgs criticised Hawking soundly, complaining that his celebrity status "gives him instant credibility that others do not have". Higgs was vindicated in 2012 when the

Fellow Cambridge alumni: Lord Martin Rees

"He was always sensitive to the misfortunes of others"

"[When I met] Hawking, he had recently been diagnosed with a degenerative disease and it was thought that he might not survive long enough to finish his degree. It was soon after I enrolled as a graduate at Cambridge University in 1964. [Hawking] was unsteady on his feet and spoke with great difficulty. Amazingly, he lived on to the age of 76. Even mere survival would have been a medical marvel, but of course he didn't just survive; he became one of the most famous scientists in the world. Astronomers are used to large numbers, but few could be large as the odds I'd have given, back in 1963 when Stephen received his 'death sentence', against witnessing this uniquely inspiring crescendo of achievement sustained for more than 50 years. Few, if any, of Einstein's successors have done more to deepen our insights into gravity, space and time.

"He was, by all accounts, a 'laid back' undergraduate, but his brilliance nonetheless earned him a first-class degree in physics, and an 'entry ticket' to a research career. Within a few years of the onset of his disease he was wheelchair-bound, and his speech was an indistinct croak that could only be interpreted by those who knew him.

"Why did he become such a 'cult figure'? The concept of an imprisoned mind roaming the cosmos plainly grabbed people's imagination. If he had achieved equal distinction in genetics rather than cosmology, his triumph of intellect against adversity probably wouldn't have achieved the same resonance with a worldwide public.

"Stephen was far from being the archetype unworldy or nerdish scientist - his personality remained amazingly unwarped by his frustrations and handicaps. As

well as his extensive travels, he enjoyed trips to theatre or opera. He had robust common sense, and was ready to express forceful political opinions. However, a downside of his iconic status was that his comments attracted exaggerated attention even on topics where he had no special expertise - for instance philosophy, or the dangers from aliens or from intelligent machines.

"But there was absolutely no gainsaying his lifelong commitment to campaigns for the disabled, and just in the last few months in support of the NHS - to which he acknowledged he owed so much. He was always, at the personal level, sensitive to the misfortunes of others. He recorded that, when in hospital soon after his illness

was first diagnosed, his depression was lifted when he compared his lot with a boy in the next bed who was dying of leukaemia.

"Tragedy struck Stephen Hawking when he was only 21. He was diagnosed with a deadly disease, and his expectations dropped to zero. He himself said that everything that happened since then was a bonus. And what a triumph his life has been. His name will live in the annals of science, millions have had their cosmic horizons widened by his best-selling books and even more around the world have been inspired by a unique example of achievement against all the odds - a manifestation of amazing willpower and determination."

The Simpsons
Episode: They Saved Lisa's Brain

The first episode of *The Simpsons* in which Hawking appeared, the 22nd episode of the cartoon's tenth season features Lisa Simpson being invited to join the Springfield chapter of Mensa. Director Pete Michels and writer Matt Selman wanted the theoretical physicist to guest-star as himself since 'they needed someone who would be smarter than all of Springfield's Mensa members and because he was a fan of the show'.

Star Trek: The Next Generation
Episode: Descent

The only person to date to have played himself on Star Trek, Hawking appeared as his own holographic counterpart in 1993 playing poker with the likes of Albert Einstein and Isaac Newton. During filming of the episode, Hawking was taken on a tour of the engineering set.

The Theory of Everything
Release date: 2 January 2015
(United Kingdom)

A British biographical romantic drama film set at Cambridge University, *The Theory of Everything* tells the story of Hawking's life. The film, in which actor Eddie Redmayne plays the physicist, was adapted from the memoir *Travelling to Infinity: My Life with Stephen* by his former spouse Jane Hawking.

Hawking in popular culture

Hawking
Release date: 13 April 2004
(United Kingdom)

In the first ever portrayal of Hawking on screen, Benedict Cumberbatch stars as the physicist during his early years as a PhD student at Cambridge. The BBC television film was nominated for Best Single Drama in the BAFTA TV Awards in 2005.

The Big Bang Theory
Episode: The Hawking Excitation

Hawking appeared in the 108th episode of the American sitcom where main character Sheldon Cooper is keen to meet his idol. In the episode, Hawking is given Sheldon's research paper on the Higgs Boson particle, where the character believes that a boson is at the centre of a black hole accelerating backwards through time.

Futurama
Episodes: Anthology of Interest I, Crimes of the Hot, The Beast with a Billion Backs, Reincarnation

Hawking featured as himself, lending his voice in several episodes in the American animated science-fiction comedy series made by *The Simpsons* creator Matt Groening.

Hawking's student: Ian Moss

"He was the definition of a genius"

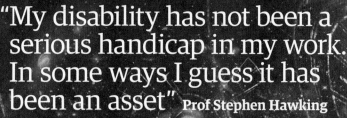

"This was a time when he could still speak, before his voice synthesiser, and only students could understand what he was saying.

"What impressed me about Stephen was that he was absolutely brilliant. Some people are very clever and you see their work and you think, 'well, if I worked really hard on that project maybe I could have done that myself'. Then there are people like Stephen, and you see his breakthroughs and you think, 'there's no way I would have thought of that if I'd spent all my life thinking on that project'."

Higgs boson was discovered at CERN, after which Hawking suggested he should win the Nobel prize in physics, which he did the next year with François Englert.

Hawking retired from the Lucasian professorship in 2009 - as stipulated in Cambridge University's regulations - having held it for 30 years, and moved on to be director of research at the Cambridge University Department of Applied Mathematics and Theoretical Physics. He continued to work through his 60s and 70s, ranging over topics such as the future of humanity, manned spaceflight, the dangers of AI and attempts to discover the unified theory, first touched upon in *A Brief History of Time*, that will bring together general relativity and quantum mechanics. He also appeared in many TV series, had a movie made about his early life and received the Presidential Medal of Freedom, America's highest civilian honour, from Barack Obama in 2009. His final scientific paper, on cosmic inflation, was published in May 2018 - just six weeks after his death in March 2018.

15 years before his death, he had already decided on his epitaph: the Bekenstein-Hawking entropy equation, or a series of numbers and letters that define Hawking radiation. "When I was 21 and contracted ALS, I felt it was very unfair," he wrote. "But now, 50 years later, I can be quietly satisfied with my life. My disability has not been a serious handicap in my scientific work. In fact, in some ways I guess it has been an asset: I haven't had to lecture or teach undergraduates, and I haven't had to sit in on tedious and time-consuming committees. I became possibly the best-known scientist in the world. This is partly because scientists, apart from Einstein, are not widely known rock stars, and partly because I fit the stereotype of a disabled genius. I can't disguise myself with a wig and dark glasses - the wheelchair gives me away."

Hawking's ashes were interred in the nave of Westminster Abbey on 15 June 2018 alongside the grave of his predecessor in both thought and professorship, Isaac Newton. His work lives on, however, and a newborn black hole in the constellation Ophiuchus, GRB180316A, has been dedicated to him. Neither can be expected to evaporate any time soon.

"My disability has not been a serious handicap in my work. In some ways I guess it has been an asset" Prof Stephen Hawking

Hawking's final theory

The universe is a hologram

It's generally believed that for a tiny fraction of a second after the Big Bang, the cosmos expanded rapidly before it settled into its current state, in what is known as inflation. On a grander scale, however, some believe that this expansion goes on forever, creating a multiverse - a theory that Hawking has never been particularly fond of.

Instead he, alongside Belgian colleague Professor Thomas Hertog, has extended the notion of a holographic reality in order to explain how the universe came into existence after the Big Bang. In this theory it's suspected that three-dimensional reality is an illusion and that the solid world around us - including the dimension of time - is projected from the information on a flat two-dimensional cosmos. With this in mind, Hawking believed that the universe arose holographically from an unknowable state outside the Big Bang.

Hawking suspected that the cosmos is holographic

DISCOVER THE PAST, PRESENT AND FUTURE OF SPACE EXPLORATION

From the formative years of Sputnik through to modern-day innovatÑns like Perseverence, embark on a journey across the history of humanity's missÑns into space, and glimpse what is in store for the future.

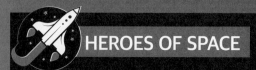

Buzz Aldrin and NASA's finest reveal...

"OUR MOST DANGEROUS MISSIONS"

In space, no one can hear you scream... which is just as well given the numerous things that can go wrong, as Buzz Aldrin, Mike Massimino, Luca Parmitano and other prolific astronauts explain

Space is well-known for its risks. As if the mental pressures of working in an isolated zero-gravity environment weren't enough, astronauts can suffer muscle loss, changes in their eyesight, radiation exposure and fluctuating blood pressure. There have also been catastrophic disasters during take off, problems with landing and mechanical failures that needed to be tackled.

However, one thing's for sure. Astronauts have come to expect the unexpected. For no matter how well prepared they and the ground crews are, and regardless of the millions of man hours that go into designing a mission, unforeseen problems can and do emerge. And when such bad luck rears its ugly head, space really can appear to be the loneliest place in the universe.

*Catch part 2 in issue 79, on sale 21 June

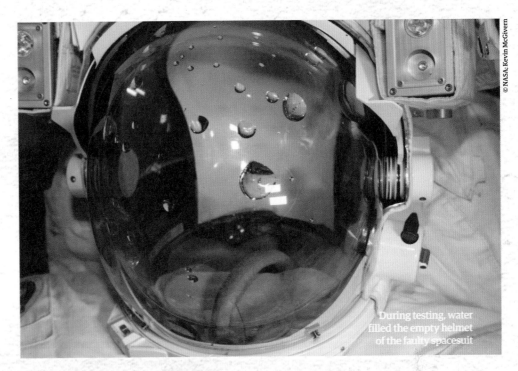

During testing, water filled the empty helmet of the faulty spacesuit

© NASA: Kevin McGivern

"I was upside down with no light, no eyesight"

Luca Parmitano recalls the moment the helmet of his Extravehicular Mobility Unit suit began filling with water

What happened?

Luca Parmitano's second EVA had to be terminated just 92 minutes into the planned 6.5-hour spacewalk when water leaked into his helmet, putting the Italian engineer and astronaut at risk of drowning. Making it difficult for him to see and hear and hindering his return to the airlock, it was later discovered that one of the suit's filters had become clogged by contamination, which had forced water from the cooling system to back up.

What mission were they on?

Expedition 36/37, working alongside fellow spacewalker Christopher Cassidy in July 2013.

"The unexpected sensation of water at the back of my neck surprised me, and I was in a place where I'd rather not be surprised. I had been out of the International Space Station for around 45 minutes to an hour on my second spacewalk when I felt it and, with superhuman effort, I forced myself to inform Houston, knowing that it could signal the end of the EVA [Extravehicular Activity].

"At the time, Chris [Cassidy] and I had no idea what was happening. At first we were both convinced that it must be drinking water from my flask that had leaked out through the straw, or else it's sweat. But, as we were waiting for advice [from Houston], I realised it wasn't going to get better. I thought the water was too cold to be sweat and, more importantly, I could feel it increasing.

"More water crawled through the back of my head over my communications cap, so we all decided, with concurrence on the ground, that it was time to go back inside and call the ground for a terminate, which is a soft word for stopping an EVA. It means putting everything back in good condition and going back inside - as opposed to an abort, which is when you leave everything as is and you go back inside and depressurise as fast as you can.

"To get back I had to go to the airlock one way and Chris had to go a different way because of the way we were routed. But, maybe a minute or two later, things began to get interesting, so to speak. I was about halfway to the airlock, becoming more and more certain that the water was increasing. I felt it covering the sponge on my earphones and I wondered whether I would lose audio content.

"Then, with the water almost completely covering the

Parmitano is also a Lieutenant Colonel in the Italian Air Force

119

How did the spacesuit helmet leak?

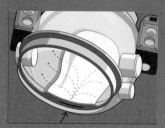

Water seepage
A port on the bottom of a space helmet allows ventilation air to flow behind the astronaut's head and blows the air in front of his or her face.

Building up
When cooling water got into the air port it began to build up, and Luca Parmitano was able to feel water at the back of his head, in his ear cups and over his eyes.

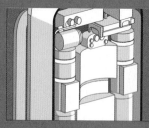

Blockage blamed
It was later found that a blockage in the spacesuit's water separator was to blame. It allowed the water to leak into the vent loop and into the helmet.

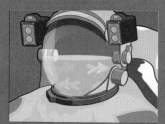

Perils of zero gravity
According to investigators, part of the problem was the way water works in zero gravity. Parmitano says it felt like being in a goldfish bowl and he feared drowning.

"I was about halfway to the airlock, becoming more and more certain that the water was increasing" Luca Parmitano

front of my visor, sticking to it and obscuring my vision, the Sun set. To understand what this means, you have to imagine an orbital sunset, which is different than Earth. You have light, then you don't. When you don't have light in orbit, it's the absolute absence of light. It's a black like nothing that you can experience when back on Earth.

"The light coming from my helmet could only illuminate a circle of light about 30-centimetres (one-foot) wide. At the same time the water covered my eyes and nose, so I was isolated in the sense that I couldn't really see well enough to navigate my own way back. I was also upside down and I had to manoeuvre myself around a no-touch zone, which is a zone that is either dangerous or you could damage some important equipment.

"So, I was upside down with no light, no eyesight because my eyes were covered. I had water in my nose. I tried to call the ground and Chris, but neither one could hear me due to water or because of the sheer geometry of the station. That's when I had to make a very

quick decision either to wait there or try to go back however I could. In a split second I came up with a decision and a plan to move and do whatever I could. I moved and decided to try to use my own capabilities to get back. About five minutes later I was back at the airlock.

"Chris arrived right away and we went inside. Chris closed the hatch and we repressurised. As soon as Karen [Nyberg] started repressurising I couldn't hear anything, so the ground was calling me, Chris was calling me, but I couldn't hear. It was pretty miserable. Water was inside my ears, inside my nose, all over my eyes, so I didn't want to move. The next thing I knew Chris was squeezing my hand trying to get a response and my response was to squeeze as hard as I could to give him the okay.

"After everyone else repressurised they opened the hatch and I saw a very worried group, Fyodor [Yurchikhin] and Karen, who quickly hurried me out of the airlock to take my helmet off, and that was the end of it."

Did you know?
Astronauts Timothy Kopra and Tim Peake had to end their spacewalk on 15 January 2016 when Kopra reported a small water bubble followed by a film of water inside his helmet. It happened after the pair had completed their main task but, as it got bigger, Mission Control decided to terminated the six-hour spacewalk an hour and 50 minutes early. Kopra was roughly 200 feet away from the ISS – about as far as a spacewalker can safely go.

Just over an hour into the spacewalk, Parmitano reported water inside his helmet on the back of his head

Massimino was forced to rip off the handrail that had a stripped screw to continue repairing Hubble

"I'd broken Hubble... and I was alone in space"

Mike Massimino had made a huge error. What's more he didn't have back up while his fellow astronauts looked on

What happened?

Mike Massimino and fellow astronaut Mike Good were completing their eight-hour, two-minute spacewalk where they sought to repair Hubble's imaging spectrograph, an instrument used to detect far-off planets and black holes. More than 100 new space tools were developed for the spacewalk, but Massimino ended up yanking a handrail away with his hands. It had been blocking the access panel to the power supply, but one of the screws was stripped, making it impossible to come off by conventional means. He did this while lapping the Earth at 28,164 kilometres (17,500 miles) per hour.

What mission were they on?

STS-125 Atlantis, the final Hubble servicing mission by the Space Shuttle, between 11 and 24 May 2009.

"We were going to use a large number of tools during a mission to repair the failed power supply of the Hubble Space Telescope, and we had practiced it for years. Although the two bolts on the top of a handrail that covered the access panel came off with no problem, and while a bolt to the left at the bottom also came out easily, the bolt on the bottom right did not. Instead, the head of the bolt was stripped out, and when I took a closer look, I spun my tool inside of it and destroyed any chance of being able to undo that screw.

"This meant the handrail wasn't going to come off and I wasn't going to be able to get

to the main electronics board. This meant we were never going to be able to replace the power supply, never get Hubble back running and never find out there was life on other planets, and I was going to be blamed. That was pretty much my thought process, but the team on the ground started to troubleshoot and I started trying not to make things worse in space.

"It took them about an hour or so to come up with a solution - and that time felt like an eternity out there. All the while the Sun's coming up and down and I'm wondering whether sooner or later we're going to have to knock it off and come inside because we were running out of time. But then they told me to get some tape and vice grips: I could understand vice grips because that was a tool. Tape, on the other hand, made me think we were running out of ideas. I didn't even know we had tape out there: were we going from the hardware store to the stationary office supplies now?

"But someone had the idea of just seeing if I could yank this thing off, and they'd worked out that about 60 pounds of force was required. So I did just that, grabbing some tape from the toolbox at the front of the space shuttle before heading back to use it on the bottom of the handrail. I felt a deep loneliness because there was no one to help me at that specific time, but

I taped the handrail, put my hand on it and knew that the reason I was using that tape was because there would be a real worry if any debris got loose. So I pulled.

"I managed to rip the handrail away; got it right off. I could then get to the access panel, but my power tool's battery had gone and I was also needing an oxygen refill. I put my fears aside, got more oxygen and swapped out the battery before getting on with the task. The screws came out, the new power supply went in and it worked - a successful mission from a position higher than the Space Station - and the instrument had come back to life. I then just looked at the Earth from 350 miles [563 kilometres] up.

"I was out there in space, all by myself, with my own life support system, and I could look anywhere I wanted. I could look and see the planet from where Hubble is. I thought, this would be the view from heaven. But then, I thought, it was more beautiful than that. It was like looking into a paradise. The brightness of the Sun when you leave the atmosphere, it's like, wow! There it is! It looks just like a star. And it's bright, really bright! It's the brightest bright I've ever experienced. Getting to see the planet and the stars on a spacewalk was truly an incredible experience."

"The tether loss was like getting hit in the stomach"

When a satellite remained inert after deployment, Jeffrey Hoffman had to perform an unplanned, untested spacewalk

What happened?

When the communication satellite Syncom IV-3 failed to activate it meant Jeff Hoffman and David Griggs were called on to perform an EVA, even though the task was something they had never done before. There was also a potential danger of the rocket engine going off.

What mission were they on?

STS-51-D between 12 and 19 April 1985, with the 16th Space Shuttle flight also suffering a ruptured tyre and brake damage on landing.

"Before every shuttle mission, two crew members were trained to use spacesuits. This meant I knew what I was doing as far as the spacesuit was concerned, but because it was the early days of the shuttle, flights kept getting postponed and cancelled. Before we actually flew in April 1985, we had been assigned to four different flights, each of which had different EVA requirements.

"Still, in my mind, if you were basically comfortable working with tools then you could go into a workshop and build something you've never built before. So while I was aware of the dangers (any time you put on a spacesuit and go outside you are in a more vulnerable situation than when you're inside your spacecraft), when the satellite did not activate on our mission and we realised we were going to have to put on a spacesuit and go outside, my general feeling was of excitement.

"Of course, you always know that something can go wrong with your spacesuit. You could also get hit by a piece of space debris. But we needed to try and sort the problem. It was definitely what we call a sporty proposition: if someone had suggested before the launch that somebody was going to go up there and do this, it may have been hard to get it approved just because it was so far out of the ordinary.

"But when we reported out of that the antenna did not pop up (it is supposed to do so two minutes after it is deployed), we knew that NASA was generally willing to pull out all the stops in order to fix a problem, and we had to work out why something had gone wrong. Either the antenna was stuck and the sequence was going as planned – which meant that in 45 minutes the rocket motors were going to fire – or the satellite never turned on.

"We didn't know which, so just for safety we moved away from the satellite. When it didn't fire 45 minutes later we knew that the whole ignition sequence was somehow blocked. The only single-point failure was a switch on the outside of the satellite which is depressed when it's in the cargo bay but opens up when deployed. It was really the only thing that we had access to because we were not planning to do a spacewalk, so we didn't have any special tools. We didn't even have any foot restraints where we could lock ourselves into a position.

"The idea of trying to go inside the satellite to do anything was out of the question, so we set out to access that switch. At first, the idea was to go on the end of the arm, hold on with one hand, fly up to the satellite and flick the switch with my other hand. That was a bit too sporty. So instead they made these two tools, which we attached to the end of the robotic arm. Our job on the EVA was to attach those tools to the end of the arm.

"We attempted this the next day, performing the rendezvous and flying up to the satellite to operate the arm that flicked that switch. It was something that nobody had ever practiced beforehand, but we just did it. Had we seen that antenna pop up then we would have known everything was okay and we would have gotten out of there in a hurry, but it never happened. We were not able to fix the problem, but we demonstrated that the switch was not the failure, so about three or four months later another crew went up, deployed their two satellites, flew to the satellite we worked on and used special equipment and foot restraints to capture it, lock it down into the cargo bay and basically hotwire the ignition circuit so that it could then be commanded from the ground.

"After they did that, they closed it up and threw it back into orbit before flying away. The ground then commanded the ignition sequence to start and the satellite went up to geostationary orbit, where it began working just fine. But our job was important. Had we not attempted to fix the obvious problem, the second crew would have been sent up to do it and it wouldn't have worked. It was a great story in the end."

Did you know?

The first spacewalk was performed by Soviet cosmonaut Alexei Leonov on 18 March 1965, but it was far from smooth flying. In the vacuum of space his spacesuit ballooned, which would prevent him from re-entering the spacecraft. Running out of time, he decided to bleed off some of the suit's pressure, risking oxygen starvation. Later on, a malfunction caused oxygen levels to soar inside the craft, increasing the possibility of a fire.

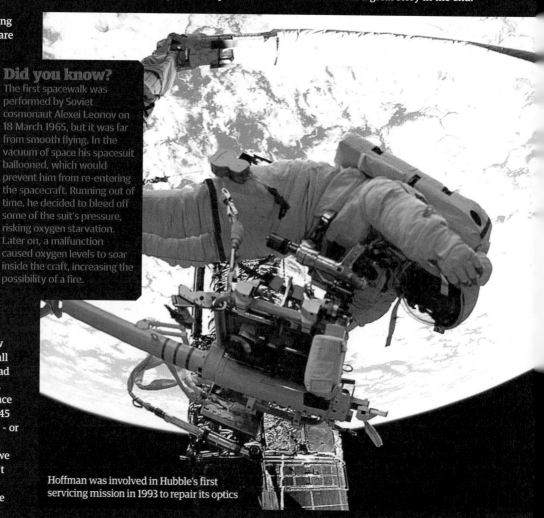

Hoffman was involved in Hubble's first servicing mission in 1993 to repair its optics

Did you know?
During Expedition 10, Chiao became the first astronaut to vote in a US Presidential election from space.

"We could have killed everyone aboard the ISS"

Leroy Chiao found himself heading at an increasing speed towards the International Space Station

What happened?

NASA astronaut Leroy Chiao and cosmonaut Salizhan Sharipov had been nearing the end of their flight to the International Space Station (ISS) when the autopilot hit a problem and began to speed up rather than slow down. With danger imminent, they had to start thinking fast.

What mission were they on?

Expedition 10, which was the tenth expedition to the ISS.

"On my last mission we were flying to the ISS in a Russian Soyuz spacecraft, TMA-5. It was Expedition 10 which began on 16 October 2004 and I was the commander and NASA science officer, flying with flight engineer Salizhan Sharipov to relieve the crewmates from the previous expedition. We were due to remain in space until 24 April 2005 - a timescale of 192 days, 19 hours and two minutes from launch to landing. It was quite a ride, and very different from the space shuttle.

"As we were approaching the ISS, the alarms started sounding with just under 200 metres [656 feet] to go. We couldn't believe it. Instead of slowing us down, the autopilot was speeding us up as we approached the station. Simultaneously it was rotating us to the left, so we were starting to lose visual sight of the ISS.

"We swung into action - we already had our emergency books in our laps - and we executed the procedure to take manual control away from the autopilot. I punched in the necessary commands while Salizhan took the hand controllers and fired braking pulses while correcting the rotation. We got the ship stopped 50 metres (164 feet) from the station, much to our relief.

"While this was going on there had been excited conversation in our headsets as the ground struggled to catch up with us. They asked us to put the ship back into autopilot. Salizhan and I looked at each other. Salizhan then asked them: "Why would we do that?" The answer was that they felt there should be no problem. Reluctantly, we re-engaged the autopilot.

"Immediately the alarms sounded again and our troubles started over. Without stopping to say anything, I took the ship back into manual mode. Salizhan and I shared another look, and we both nodded. It was understood between us that we wouldn't do that again, even if the ground demanded it.

"We then executed the first manual night docking to the ISS. After we were safely docked, I took a deep breath. The hairs on the back of my neck suddenly stood up and I began to shiver. It was then that I realised that this had been a very dangerous situation. If we had collided with the International Space Station, then we almost certainly would have been killed. Not only that, we could have killed everyone aboard the ISS too."

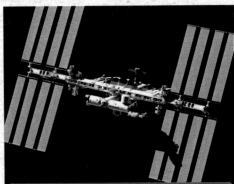

Good vibrations: how Chiao shook the ISS

When a solar array was left half-exposed and in mid-retraction above the International Space Station in 2006, mission controllers turned to a method that had been inadvertently developed by Leroy Chiao two years earlier.

Believing friction between the P6 array's guide wires was to blame, they reckoned getting an astronaut to go through a vigorous exercise workout could relieve the tension and allow the array to fold up properly. Why? Because Chiao had shook the space station a couple of years earlier by doing the exact same thing.

"I was doing squats on the Interim Resistance Excercise Device (IRED) and accidentally hit the resonant frequency of the station (about 1Hz)," he says. "The entire stack started shaking, and Salizhan reported that he could see the modules flex as he looked down the centerline from the Service Module."

Although Mission Control had told him to "knock it off" at the time, German ESA astronaut Thomas Reiter was asked to perform 30 seconds of robust exercise on the IRED bungee bar. It took a spacewalk to finally retract the array, but it was certainly a novel potential solution.

"The fuel tank was running low. Then there was a problem with the hatch"

Buzz Aldrin and fellow astronaut Neil Armstrong were seconds away from crashing into the Moon - and worried they wouldn't get home

What happened?

As Neil Armstrong and Buzz Aldrin looked to land the lunar module Eagle on the Moon, leaving Michael Collins in the command module, they found they were landing miles west of their target site, running out of fuel and desperate to touch down. With the computer about to put them in an area strewn with boulders, manual action had to be taken. Later, they discovered a vital component had accidentally been damaged.

What mission were they on?

Apollo 11, the mission that landed the first two humans on the Moon, on 20 July 1969.

Apollo 11 was the fifth manned mission of the Apollo program

"About four minutes into the landing sequence of Apollo 11, the display on the computer read 1201 and 1202. They were error codes, the number of the alarm, and whatever information was displayed before - whether it was velocity or movement over the ground - was not there any more.

"These codes were disturbing and distracting, but Mission Control didn't know what the alarms meant either. Neil Armstrong, who was paying more attention than I was since he was looking out of the window, took manual control. There were craters drifting by, but not many of them were identifiable. Neil said he thought we may be a little long: the Eagle had overshot its planned landing site.

"The fuel tank was running low and Neil understood this. By experience, there were two minutes of fuel remaining and ahead was a crater that looked dangerous with giant rocks around it. The easiest thing to do was just slow the rate of descent and fly over whatever it was, but that would take longer and burn more fuel and make fuel quantity at touchdown a little less. We were just over 30 metres (100 feet) from the surface, and Neil had to land somewhere.

"I could see the shadow getting bigger because the Sun was behind us, and we were getting closer and closer to the shadow of the lander. The dust began kicking up and, without trying to disturb Neil's concentration, I gave him a little body language to get on the ground as soon as possible. And then it happened. We touched down safely in the Sea of Tranquillity. There had been just 15 seconds of fuel spare.

"We then had a problem with the hatch. The pressure inside had to be low, but when we tried to pull the hatch down it wouldn't come open. I bent the door back and equalised the pressure. I watched out the window to see Neil go down the ladder. When it was my turn to back out, I remember the checklist said to reach back carefully and close the hatch, being careful not to lock it. It would have been very difficult to open it from the outside if I had.

"The Moon's surface can be best described as utter desolation, with no signs of life whatsoever. There were a few hours to collect precious rock samples and carry out experiments. Once we were ready, I looked around at some of the lunar dust on the ground and saw the broken end of a circuit breaker. One of the spacesuits had knocked it out, but it was needed to start the engine and get us back home. The broken parts that were still on the inside had to be pushed in, and only two people could fix this. "So, in the countdown procedure, I used a pen to push the circuit breaker in. This worked and the engine started. We could go home."

Communion on the Moon

Before Neil Armstrong set foot on the Moon and uttered his legendary words on 20 July 1969, Buzz Aldrin had opened a plastic container of wine and bread which he had obtained from Webster Presbyterian Church near Houston. He opened up communication with NASA and requested a few moments of contemplative silence before eating and drinking. "It was interesting to think that the very first liquid ever poured on the Moon, and the first food eaten there, were communion elements," he explained. This act was not broadcast, however, and NASA sought not to reveal the news because there was a danger of inflaming atheist Madalyn Murray O'Hair, who had already become incensed that the Apollo 8 crew had read the Genesis creation account and filed a lawsuit.

How to get off the Moon with a pen

Identify the problem
Make some final checks of your cramped spacecraft. Perhaps the bulky spacesuits have brushed too harshly against the switch to the circuit breaker, snapping it.

Figure out its severity
Now look at the circuit breaker in closer detail. This activates the ascent engine and needs to be pushed in. Can that be achieved? Consider how it can be done.

Use that pen
Stop chewing on that felt pen while you think. Maybe it can be used in some way. Just make sure it does not have metal on the end; you're dealing with electrics.

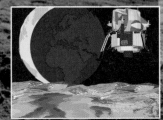

Insert the pen
Put the chrome-bodied pen into the small opening where the circuit breaker should be. Now push and, with a bit of luck, the circuit breaker will hold. Time to get going.

Skylab plummeted back to Earth over Australia in July 1979

"We both went ass over teakettle into outer space"

After fixing a solar array it suddenly deployed, throwing Joseph Kerwin and Pete Conrad off the Skylab hull

What happened?
After Pete Conrad and Joseph Kerwin had attempted to free a stuck solar array by tugging at it with a hooked pole, a second EVA was sanctioned and proved more successful. But not before the solar array deployed and knocked the pair into space. Could their safety tethers hold?

What mission were they on?
Skylab 2, which launched on 25 May 1973 and was the first manned mission to the first US orbital space station, Skylab.

Kerwin was the first physician selected for astronaut training

"The Skylab space station orbited the Earth from 1973 to 1979 and it had a workshop, a solar observatory, a multiple docking adapter and the ability to allow three crews to stay for up to 84 days in space. But after it launched, a solar array became stuck in the wrong position. It also appeared that the meteoroid protective shield had prematurely deployed, too.

"For that reason the launch of Skylab 2, with myself, Charles Conrad and Paul Weitz, had to be postponed. But we spent the time practicing using special tools that would remove the material jamming the solar array so that Skylab would gain the necessary electrical power. The actual act would mean us performing an EVA to free, and that was always going to be dangerous.

"There were no handholds, no footholds, no visual aids and no lights because there was never any planned maintenance on Skylab. But, because there was a planned EVA to retrieve film and exchange film in the Apollo Telescope Mount, we had the suits, we had the umbilicals and we brought up some tools that we thought we'd need.

"We launched the mission on 25 May 1973.

Kerwin removes metal from the solar array to allow Skylab's solar panels to fully deploy

© NASA; Nicholas Forder

A new solar shield was deployed and then the spacewalk to free the jammed solar array began. I cut the metal that had jammed the solar wing in a folder position and we'd attempted to use a 7.5-metre (25-foot) pole with a cable cutter on the end of it and some rope to force the array beam to deploy. But getting the jaws on to the strap at a six-metre (20-foot) distance with a pole and no foot restraints was proving impossible so, after sitting around thinking about it, we decided to use an eyebolt we'd found on the surface of the workshop near one of the antennas.

"We didn't know what the eye bolt was there for, but the plan was to strap myself to it. So we got the spare tether, and there was a hook on the front of the suit. I hooked it through there, ran it through the eye bolt, back up through the suit, tightened it up and now I had a three-point suspension. I could stand. I could place my feet on the surface of the workshop and almost straighten my knees all the way out and suddenly I'm as stable as a rock. It was wonderful. Two minutes later the job was done, but as we crawled under the rope that Pete had laid out and stood up, suddenly it released on us.

"We both went ass over teakettle into outer space, but our EVA system was an umbilical, a nice stout umbilical with an eighth-inch [three millimetre] steel cable in the middle of it, so we didn't have any worries about that. We went out to the end of our umbilicals, and then hand-over-handed ourselves back until we got something to hang on to. Turned around, and the prettiest sight I've ever seen in my life was that solar panel cover fully deployed, and you could see the panels starting to come out as they warmed up in the Sun. And we knew we had done the job."

Did you know?

The crew of Apollo 13 — Fred Haise, Jack Swigert and Jim Lovell — currently hold the record for the farthest distance reached from Earth by humans. Scheduled to be NASA's third manned Moon mission, the crew were forced to abort when an oxygen tank exploded, crippling the spacecraft and threatening the lives of its crew. They reached the far side of the Moon — a distance of 400,171 kilometres (248,655 miles) from Earth in April 1970.

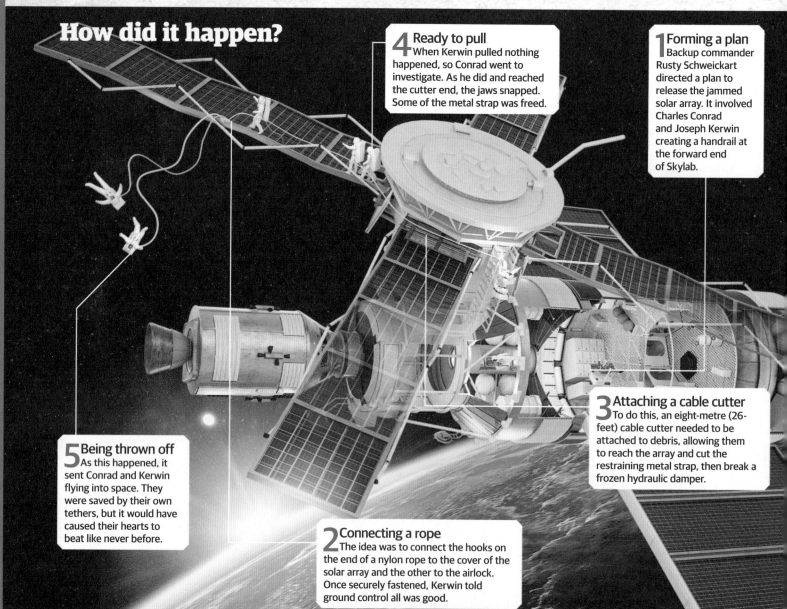

How did it happen?

4 Ready to pull
When Kerwin pulled nothing happened, so Conrad went to investigate. As he did and reached the cutter end, the jaws snapped. Some of the metal strap was freed.

1 Forming a plan
Backup commander Rusty Schweickart directed a plan to release the jammed solar array. It involved Charles Conrad and Joseph Kerwin creating a handrail at the forward end of Skylab.

3 Attaching a cable cutter
To do this, an eight-metre (26-feet) cable cutter needed to be attached to debris, allowing them to reach the array and cut the restraining metal strap, then break a frozen hydraulic damper.

5 Being thrown off
As this happened, it sent Conrad and Kerwin flying into space. They were saved by their own tethers, but it would have caused their hearts to beat like never before.

2 Connecting a rope
The idea was to connect the hooks on the end of a nylon rope to the cover of the solar array and the other to the airlock. Once securely fastened, Kerwin told ground control all was good.

Apollo 13 is possibly the most famous of NASA's dangerous missions. Here the capsule is retrieved after splashdown by crewmen from the USS Iwo Jima

Find out everything you've ever wanted to know about outer space

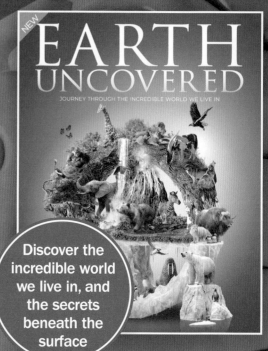

Discover the incredible world we live in, and the secrets beneath the surface

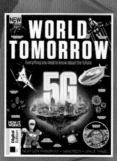

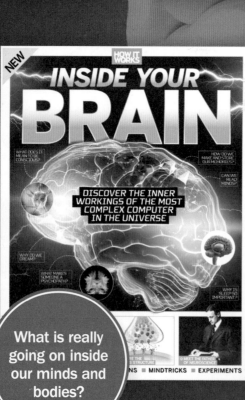

What is really going on inside our minds and bodies?

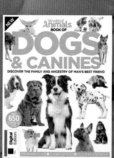

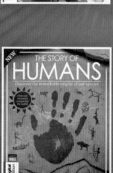

Get great savings when you buy direct from us

1000s of great titles, many not available anywhere else

World-wide delivery and super-safe ordering

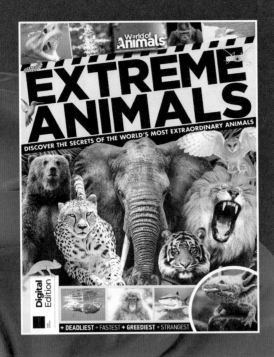
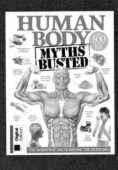
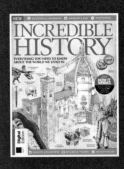

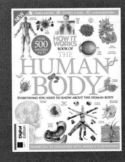